One Day In
Oradour

First published 2013 by
A & C Black, an imprint of Bloomsbury Publishing Plc
50 Bedford Square, London, WC1B 3DP

www.bloomsbury.com

ISBN 978-1-4081-8201-7

A CIP catalogue for this book is available from the British Library.

Printed and bound by CPI Group (UK) Ltd, Croydon CR0 4YY

1 3 5 7 9 10 8 6 4 2

MIX
Paper from
responsible sources
FSC® C020471

One Day In Oradour

Helen Watts

A & C BLACK
AN IMPRINT OF BLOOMSBURY
LONDON NEW DELHI NEW YORK SYDNEY

DEDICATION

For the 206 children of Oradour-sur-Glane whose
lives were cut so cruelly short on 10th June 1944
and for my own children, Jack and Georgia.

May the stories of children lost teach those
who will guide our future.

AUTHOR'S NOTE

The following story is based on true events. However, the
names of the characters and many of the locations have
been changed, as have certain physical characteristics
and other descriptive details. Some of the events and
characters are also composites of several individual
events or persons, and some events and characters are
completely fictional.

CONTENTS

PART 5
SATURDAY 10 JUNE, 1944 (LATE AFTERNOON)

PART 6
SATURDAY 10 JUNE, 1944 (EVENING)

PART 7
THURSDAY 29 JUNE, 1944 (DUSK)

PART 8
EPILOGUE

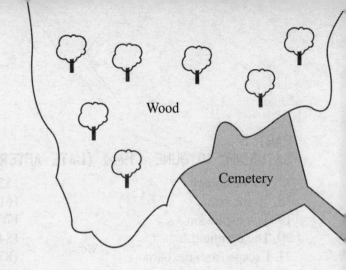

Wood

Cemetery

Farmland

Fairground

Paddocks

5

3 **4** Rue Depaul **8**

1 **2** **6** **7**

← To Confolens

To Saint Junien

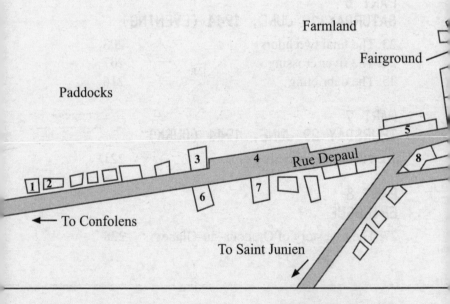

Key:

1 The Fournier cottage
2 Guy Dupont's cottage
3 Post office
4 Tram station
5 Hotel de la Glane

6 Dr Bertrand Depaul's house and surgery
7 Village hall
8 Monsieur Demarais' wine store
9 Dr Henri Depaul's house (Mayor)
10 Rachael and Ethan's house
11 Girls' school

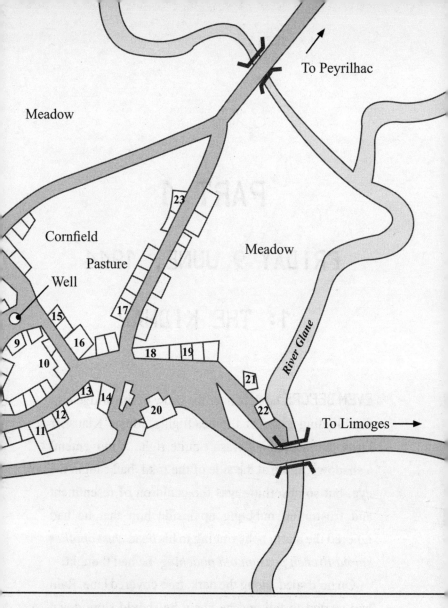

To Peyrilhac

Meadow

Meadow

Cornfield

Pasture

Well

River Glane

To Limoges

12 Patric Depaul's garage
13 Jean Neville's barber's shop
14 Denis Babin's barn
15 Stonemason's workshop
16 Monsieur Joubert's barn
17 Benoit and Blanche
Martin's house

18 Blacksmith's forge
19 The Martin bakery
20 Church
21 Mill barn
22 Mill
23 Alfred's school

PART 1

FRIDAY 9 JUNE, 1944

1: THE KIDNAP

EVEN BEFORE he flew over the brow of the bridge into the blinding glare of the headlights, Major Klausner knew that something wasn't quite right. A movement, a shadowy figure at the side of the road, had caught his eye, but so absorbing was the cauldron of resentment and frustration bubbling up inside him that he had ignored the alarm bells ringing in his head. *Just another stupid French peasant out poaching*, he had thought.

On he'd sped, along the dark, tree-covered lane. Rain had started to fall and he knew he should slow down but he just wanted to get back to base, back to Limoges. He had already wasted enough time for one day and he needed to clear his head and start drawing up some plans of his own. Next time he wasn't going to miss the chance to show the men in 3rd Battalion why he'd been made their commander. And he was desperate to teach some of those loathsome Resistance fighters a lesson.

For days, the French Resistance had been hampering the progress of the SS battalions as they marched north to Normandy to defend against the Allied invasion. Speed was of the essence and yet the German troops were having to cope with ambush after ambush.

The previous day, Klausner's friend Major Dietrich had come under attack while leading his battalion across the Dordogne river. The poor swine had been totally exposed out there on the bridge, with nowhere to shelter, when the Resistance opened fire. And they had only just regrouped when they came under a second attack on the north side of the river. Thankfully, and in typical fashion, Dietrich had made sure that the river bank was littered with French bodies before moving on.

Then this other Resistance cell had had the gall to attack the German garrison in Guéret, and Klausner had been summoned immediately to the division headquarters in Limoges.

'You have complete authority to re-take the garrison and annihilate them,' Major General Scholz had said, waving a copy of a memo he had received a few days before from General Müller, who commanded the entire Das Reich division within the SS. 'Remember, these Resistance fighters are illegal combatants. They are defying the 1940 Armistice that their own country signed.'

As he stood before Scholz's desk, Klausner had had to clench his jaw to prevent the smile from curling around his lips and his stomach had lurched with a rush of excitement. This was his chance to strike back. Justice would be brought. The Resistance would be left in no doubt that any more attacks around this region were a very bad idea.

Swiftly, Klausner had mustered a small convoy and headed for Guéret. They made good progress on the quiet, evening roads and took no time at all to surround the garrison.

But the siege was over before they even entered the building. The sound of their vehicles flying into the courtyard and pulling up abruptly on the gravel had alarmed the Resistance fighters. Momentarily distracted by the noise from outside, the gang leader lowered his guard long enough for the commander of the garrison to overpower him, killing him with one shot to the chest at close range from his own gun.

With their leader dead, and realising that they were outnumbered, the remaining gang members lost their nerve. Two surrendered immediately to the garrison commander and it took only minutes for the rest to be rounded up. So by the time Klausner and his men got inside, the garrison was already back under control.

Klausner knew that his words of praise to the commander should have been heart-felt, but even as he uttered them he could feel the resentment rising in his throat. He hated the Resistance and their underhand tactics. Too spineless to stand up and fight in public for their country, too cowardly to battle face to face, army to army, they chose instead to strike in the night, to lay traps and to pick off their targets from afar. How dare they call themselves heroes! How he would have loved to be the one to teach them a lesson here tonight… to show them what a true hero looked like.

Spinning on the heels of his highly polished SS boots, Klausner had stormed out of the garrison, barking at his men to follow him, then leapt into the closest vehicle and sped off.

Now, alone, and several kilometres ahead of the rest of the returning convoy, Klausner knew he had hit the bridge too fast to be able to stop himself careering into the road block ahead. Dazzled by the lights, he would have to take his chances and swerve.

Trees to the right. Open darkness to the left.

13

He braced himself, slammed on the brakes and turned the steering wheel. The front tyres hit the grassy bank at the side of the road, throwing Klausner first forwards, and then sideways as the brakes finally bit and the jeep span to a halt. A jolt of pain ran through his shoulder where it had struck the side of the jeep and his neck felt numb.

He blinked repeatedly, disoriented by the lights. He could just make out the shape of a small delivery van, with a car parked either side of it, all facing the bridge, engines running. Klausner heard footsteps approaching fast. He had to get out. He slid his hand into his jacket to draw his pistol while desperately groping for the door lever.

'Don't move!' screamed a voice in his ear. The attacker went straight for Klausner's hand and twisted his wrist, jerking his arm behind his back as he slammed the Major's head into the steering wheel. Pain shot through Klausner's eyes and nose and a salty trickle of blood immediately ran down onto his upper lip.

The door was wrenched open by a second attacker who snatched the keys from the ignition. Klausner's hands were tied behind his back and his pistol removed from his jacket.

While the second attacker held Klausner's own pistol to his temple, the first yanked him upright before grabbing him by the collar and dragging him out of the jeep. He breathed heavily as he pulled Klausner up onto his feet. Standing behind him he put his lips against Klausner's ear and spat out some words in German, spoken with a thick French accent.

'You're coming with us, Major. Don't make a sound.'

'Come, Alexis, we must go,' said the second attacker. 'The others can't be far behind.' He moved round in front of Klausner as he spoke, and Klausner could see that he was much smaller than the man holding him, but fit and well-toned. His face was narrow, his features pointed, the tip of his nose slightly up-turned and shrew-like, and he wore a lumpy woollen hat pulled down low over his intense, beady little eyes. Klausner noticed a dark, raised line of flesh across the man's cheek. A fresh scar, just beginning to heal.

Klausner knew these were Resistance fighters. If he was lucky they were taking him hostage. If not, he was a dead man. His best hope was to go quietly and buy himself time.

Two more men, both dressed completely in black, with leather jackets and felt berets, helped to bundle Klausner into the back of the delivery van, then the smaller of his two assailants climbed into the driver's seat. Klausner counted five others getting into the cars.

As the doors on the rear of the van were slammed

shut and bolted, another man jumped into the passenger seat beside the driver. 'Quick! Quick!' he screamed. 'Headlights. The other edge of the woods. Go, go, go!'

This must have been the lookout – the figure in the trees – who Klausner had passed on the lane before he reached the bridge.

Klausner tried to sit up to see out of the tiny window in between him and the front cab of the van but, not being able to use his hands to hold himself up, he was instantly thrown to the floor again as the van did a violent U-turn to make its escape.

Klausner quickly lost track of where he was as the van made countless twists and turns down the winding country lanes. He was not surprised that his captors were avoiding the main roads. Very soon the entire Das Reich division would know that his jeep had been found abandoned and the whole area between Guéret and Limoges would be under search.

He had to think fast.

He groped in the dark for anything which might function as a weapon but found only empty sacks and something like grain or seed spilled all over the floor. There was a sweet, earthy smell, too. Klausner guessed he was in some kind of farm vehicle.

Finding nothing useful, Klausner began instead to work at the rope which bound his hands. He twisted and pulled his wrists this way and that behind his back until he could feel the knots loosening and the rope starting to slacken. His skin burned with pain and he had to grit his teeth, but eventually he could feel a hand starting to slide. One more tug and twist and he was free.

Underneath him, Klausner could feel the road surface change and he heard a car pass in the other direction. Were they coming into a town? Slowly and quietly, he lifted himself up and peeped out of the tiny window.

He knew where he was. They had brought him right into Limoges!

Klausner felt in all his pockets, looking for something that might help him escape. He had nothing on him apart from his identity papers. Could those save his life? They could certainly help him to be found.

After another ten minutes or so, the van slowed and turned up a side street. The driver and the lookout both got out, and Klausner listened intently to their boots on the cobbles as they walked round to the back of the van. He had to be ready.

He pulled himself up into a crouching position and the second he heard the bolt being drawn he lunged at the doors, bursting out into the fresh air. His captors were taken aback, and the lookout stumbled as Klausner fell, head-first, into him, driving the air from his chest.

But the driver's reactions were too quick. As the struggling men fell to the ground, the driver pistol-whipped Klausner across the back of the head.

Stunned, Klausner rolled off the lookout and into the gutter. His vision was blurred but as he looked up into the night sky he could just make out the moon coming out from behind the clouds.

Then everything went dark again as one of the sacks from the back of the van was pulled down over his head.

'Tie the filthy Fritz up again,' ordered the driver through gritted teeth. 'And this time, make sure he can't get out.'

Once again the earthy smell from the back of the van filled Klausner's nostrils and he struggled to breathe as the rough cloth was pulled tightly against his face. His starched officer's jacket was scrunched up under his arms, but he managed to keep one arm up inside the sack before it was tied around his chest. He could still reach his pocket, and his papers.

At that moment, a car screeched to a halt beside them. Klausner's heart skipped a beat, hoping that this was the moment he would be rescued.

'Get him in, now!' A woman's voice, French. 'There's been a change of plan. We're taking him on to Breuilaufa. Limoges is too dangerous. It's crawling with the SS. Seems like we've caught ourselves a rather big fish.'

Klausner was shoved in the direction of the voice then pushed into the back of a car. A body got in behind him and the door was pulled shut. Then Klausner heard the now familiar voice of the lookout speaking through the window:

'Who the devil is he, then?'

'Only the highest-ranking SS commander ever kidnapped by the Resistance,' gloated the woman. 'We'll be famous after this, Jean. Now get out of here while you still can.'

'What shall I do with the van?' called the lookout, as the car started to pull away.

The woman laughed out of the open window. 'Burn it. Like we will burn him!'

Klausner went cold. He knew now that he had just one chance. Someone had to find the papers he had dropped.

Left behind in the gutter was the only clue to tracking the kidnappers of Major Thomas Klausner.

2: SYLVIE FOURNIER

SYLVIE FOURNIER was tired and more than a little frazzled. Sunday would be the feast day of Corpus Christi and she had worked all day mending, washing and ironing the family's clothes ready for Mass. Three of her children – Christelle, Sabine and Alfred – had been invited to walk behind the procession after the service, which also meant making each of them a flower garland to carry.

Sylvie had already spent far too long scouring the fields around the village, looking for a pretty selection of flowers and greenery, and it didn't help that she kept bumping into her neighbours, who all wanted to stop and chat.

'It's going to be busy here tomorrow,' Madame Babin, the clog-maker's wife, remarked as she met Sylvie on the bridge which crossed the river Glane on the edge of the village. 'Doctor Depaul says there could be over a hundred children coming into Oradour for that health and vaccination programme he's running. How's he going to get through them all, that's what I want to know.'

Sylvie shrugged and shook her head. However many children there were, she was sure Doctor Depaul would have it all organised. He would be running those health checks like a military machine.

When she escaped from Madame Babin's chattering, Sylvie walked on along the river bank, smiling to herself as she remembered the look of horror on Alfred's face that morning when she'd told him that there was a health inspection in school on Saturday.

He had been sitting at the kitchen table eating his breakfast, his red hair all ruffled from the previous night's sleep. Three-year-old Paulette was sitting next to him sipping her warm milk, her mouth painted with a glistening, creamy smile, while Louis, exactly one year older than his sister but only a centimetre taller, was happily driving a wooden truck round and round his piece of bread and jam.

'Argh, Maman, do I *have* to have an injection?' Alfred had pleaded. 'Having a health check is bad enough. We have to line up and wait for ages for our turn and I hate having to be prodded and poked about by that nasty old man. And this time it's going to be worse than ever… he's going to jab a horrid great needle into my arm!'

'I'm sure you won't make a fuss though, Alfie,' she had said, giving him a wink. 'You're the big boy of the family, so I know you'll be brave.'

Alfred had let out a long sigh, but said no more.

By the time she reached the water mill at the other end of the meadow, Sylvie had filled her basket with flowers and grasses and she was starting to feel thirsty in the late afternoon heat. A fit and nimble woman, just thirty-five years of age, Sylvie loved being out in the fresh air, but her blonde hair and fair complexion meant she had to take care in the strong sun.

Lifting the hem of her cotton summer dress, she climbed over the low fence at the back of the water mill and started back up the lane into Oradour. She followed the high retaining wall which ran in front of the church. The sky over the village ahead of her was a beautiful deep blue and Sylvie tilted her head back, turning her freckly nose upwards to take in the air. The aroma of the early summer crops mixed deliciously with the scent from the flowers in her basket and for a moment she closed her eyes and thought how lucky her family was to have found refuge in such a perfect little place.

As she came to the end of the church wall Sylvie almost collided with Audrey Rousseau, who was hurrying down the sloping pathway out of the churchyard.

'Ah, Madame Fournier,' said Audrey. 'Getting ready for Sunday, I presume?' Then, without waiting for an answer, 'I'm glad I've bumped into you. I was wondering if you could help me tomorrow afternoon with the church flowers for the festival. I've been in there cleaning all morning and Madame Renard from the boys' school said she would give me a hand tomorrow with the arrangements, but of course now she has to help Dr Depaul. It's most inconvenient. Do be a dear and say yes. It would really get me out of a hole.'

'Of course,' said Sylvie, wishing she had gone the other way and avoided bumping into Audrey. The other woman was several years her elder and had lived in Oradour all her life. Nothing happened in the village which Audrey did not know about, and she had an opinion on everything – usually a strong one. Sylvie found her intimidating.

Not that Audrey had ever been anything but kind to her. In fact, when Sylvie, Leon and the children had first come to live in Oradour, it was Audrey who had paid their first two weeks' rent on the new cottage until Leon began his job at the bakery. For that Sylvie would always be utterly grateful. But somehow with Audrey, every kindness seemed to come with an obligation.

When Leon and Sylvie Fournier had first arrived at their little stone cottage in Rue Depaul, they had certainly been in need of some help and kindness. They had fled to Oradour from their home in Charly in north-east France with their three children – Christelle, the eldest, Sabine, now eleven and young Alfred, now seven. The whole region of Lorraine had been annexed by the Nazis. All Jews were being deported and any French residents, like the Fourniers, who refused to live under the authority of the Reich were thrown out of their homes. The Nazis simply gave their houses away, to people they considered to be more deserving – the 'good' and the 'faithful', they called them.

When the Germans arrived in Charly, hammering on every door and searching every home in the village, the Fourniers were given just one hour to pack before they were cast out onto the street. No one was allowed to take more than thirty kilograms of possessions. So, in a state of wild panic and while trying to keep the children calm, Leon and Sylvie had to rush about the house making frantic decisions about which items were essential and which had such sentimental value that they couldn't bear to leave them behind.

The family was too poor to own a car, so they had made the first part of their journey out of Charly on foot, with the heavily pregnant Sylvie holding little Alfred's hand, and Christelle and Sabine struggling to help their father carry the hastily-packed bags. Desperate, and with the frightened children in tears, Leon and Sylvie had no idea where to go but they could hear enough shouting, and then gunfire, behind them to know that they had to keep on moving as fast as they could.

They headed south, out of Lorraine, walking for the rest of the day. As night fell, they reached a railway station on the outskirts of Metz. While Sylvie and the children tried to get some rest, using their luggage as makeshift pillows, Leon went off to find the ticket office, hoping and praying that they could get a train that night which would take them far enough away to find safety.

A long queue had already formed at the counter – dozens of families, men, women and children, all looking as confused, dishevelled and frantic as Leon. An elderly Jewish couple held onto one another in the queue in front of him.

'Excuse me. Can I ask you where you are going?' Leon had said, his voice trembling. 'I feel so useless. I don't even know what tickets to ask for. I have three children with me and I'm so worried about my wife. She's pregnant, you see. Where can I take them where they'll be safe?'

The old man reached out and touched Leon's arm.

'It will be all right,' he said quietly. 'Have you got money for tickets?'

'Yes, I think so,' said Leon. 'I mean, I hope it's enough. It's all the savings I have.'

'Then come with us,' whispered the old man, peering at Leon kindly over his spectacles. 'My name's Ethan. I have a brother, Joseph. He's a refugee, too, but he's found somewhere safe to live, for now at least. A place called Oradour. Not far from Limoges. He says it's peaceful there... no trouble from the Resistance, and the Germans leave it alone. It's a long way but we know which route to take. My wife Rachael and I can help you and your family to get there, at least. Besides, it sounds like your family could be good company for us. It'll be nice to have some young 'uns to talk to.' The old man smiled as the relief showed on Leon's face.

Three days later, the Fournier family and their two new companions got off the tram that had brought them from Limoges into Oradour. They had travelled over one thousand kilometres, almost to the other side of France. Exhausted, scared and hungry and with hardly a thing to their name, they began the first day of their new life in the village which would become their very last family home.

3: ALFRED FOURNIER

SYLVIE WAS a patient woman. She had to be, with five children and a husband to care for. But sometimes even her patience was sorely tested, and this was one of those occasions. She had finished the long day's work and made the garlands, then cooked the children's supper and was now about to serve it, yet once again there was no sign of Alfred.

'It's just typical!' she snapped, as she took the pot off the stove to stop the fish stew from drying up while she went outside to look for him. 'After all the rushing about I've done today! That boy will never learn to be on time.'

Sylvie peered over the fence at the bottom of the garden, searching in vain for a glimpse of Alfred's red hair in the paddock behind the cottage. Squinting, she cast her eye along the edge of the woods on the brow of the hill behind the cemetery. Again, nothing. She wiped her hands on her apron. *Bother*, she thought, knowing that the dinner was definitely going to be ruined. She would have to send Christelle out to look for him.

Most of the mothers in Oradour would simply feed their other children and teach Alfred a lesson by serving his meal up cold when he came home – or by sending him to bed without any supper at all. But Sylvie was too anxious about Alfred's safety to think of punishing him – for now, at least. She couldn't assume that he was late, sit back and wait. She had to be sure he was alright.

For Sylvie knew that life could change in an instant; that one moment you could be going about your day without a care and the next moment your world could be turned upside down. There was no getting away from it, bad things *could* happen to you. So when Sylvie set her children a curfew, she expected them to stick to it. And they usually did… except for Alfred. Sylvie had lost count of the number of times she'd warned him not to wander too far. 'What if the Germans came,' she would say, 'and you were miles away?'

Alfred was a good boy really. Small for his age, with thick, floppy red hair, he always took it on his small shoulders to look after everyone whenever his father was at work or away on his delivery rounds. Little Louis and Paulette adored him and followed him everywhere around the cottage, while Sabine and Christelle liked to poke fun at him, affectionately calling him '*petit papa*'.

Sometimes it saddened Sylvie that she never saw Alfred playing the fool or just being silly in the way that seven-year-olds should. It was as if, in the upheaval of the move to Oradour, he had left behind his ability to be light-hearted. Even his smile had changed. Now the joyous dimples in his cheeks were offset by a slight narrowing of his eyes, a questioning dip in the eyebrows. It was as if Alfred couldn't take anything at face value any more.

But this inquisitiveness led to an unquenchable thirst for exploration and Alfred took every opportunity he could to head off and investigate. He would spend hours walking the fields and meadows surrounding the village, clambering along the river bank, climbing trees and discovering new routes along the little paths and alleyways between the buildings.

Although Sylvie worried about him when he was off on one of his adventures, she admired his curiosity and his boldness. Alfred had made so many friends in Oradour that people who Sylvie had never seen before would come up to her in the street and ask, 'How's Alfie?' or 'What's that lad of yours been up to lately? He hasn't been to visit for a while.'

Yes, he was popular, all right. And Sylvie knew that Alfred was never deliberately late home. He would just get carried away and lose track of time.

Alfred understood his mother's anxiety. That last day in Charly was etched in his memory. He could recall clinging on to his mother's hand and wondering why she was dragging him so roughly down the street. He had been sobbing, 'Ruffe, Ruffe, I want to get Ruffe,' but all his mother kept saying was, 'It's too late, darling, we can't go back. I will have to knit you another Ruffe.'

Ruffe was Alfred's little stuffed dog. He was made from the softest red-brown wool and Alfred had had him since he was a baby. He was missing a button eye and had long since lost his tail, but Alfred loved Ruffe dearly and couldn't get to sleep without him. Sylvie had knitted him a new Ruffe when they settled in Oradour, but it wasn't the same and, although Alfred kept the new Ruffe on his bed (mainly so as not to hurt his mother's feelings), he found that looking at him just made him sad. 'Besides,' Alfred told himself, 'I am a big boy now and I don't need a silly toy dog to get to sleep.'

No, Alfred didn't underestimate what could happen if the Germans came into his life again. But he wasn't afraid. If they ever marched into Oradour, he and his brothers and sisters all knew what to do. Their parents had made sure of that.

'If you see any Germans you must run away, no matter what you are doing, or where you are,' their father had told them.

And nearly every time Alfred or his elder sisters went out to play, their mother would remind them of their family pact to meet in the woods behind the cemetery if there were ever any danger. By crossing the paddock at the back of their cottage you could sneak along a wall, hidden from sight, away from all the houses on Rue Depaul and across the field to the cemetery. You didn't need to go through the village at all. 'If your father and I are not here,' she would say, 'you older ones must make sure that Louis and Paulette aren't left behind. You know what those Germans are capable of. They won't care that you're just children.'

So Alfred didn't mean to upset his mother, or intend to be late home that day. However, after school, he decided to visit the barber's shop. The owner, Jean Neville, was always happy for Alfred to stop by. He let Alfred whip up the soap if a client wanted a shave, and Alfred liked chatting to all the customers while Jean snipped away with his scissors.

There was Monsieur Babin, the clog-maker, who liked to go fishing on his days off. He could name all the types of fish in the River Glane and the best places to catch them. He liked his hair short at the back and sides.

Then there was Monsieur Demarais, who owned the wine storehouse and who came every Friday for a shave but never paid. Instead, a bottle wrapped in brown paper would be handed to Jean, accompanied by a wink and a nod. He liked to grow his hair long on one side and have it combed right over the top of his head. Monsieur Demarais was old now, and didn't often leave Oradour, but in his youth he had travelled far and wide, buying wines from all the different regions of France. He entranced Alfred with his vivid descriptions of all the delicious smells, colours and exquisite flavours he had sampled and the passion with which he talked about some of his favourite vintages.

And on rare occasions there was Pierre Petit, the farmer, who hated having his hair cut and would let it grow in curly black locks way down over his collar until, threatened by his wife with a pair of shearing scissors, he gave in. While he sat rigidly in the barber's chair, Pierre would welcome the distraction of Alfred's endless questions about the plants, birds and insects he had seen in the fields and woodlands around Oradour. Pierre was a fountain of knowledge, a walking encyclopaedia of nature. Alfred wished that Pierre would wear his hair shorter or choose a more complicated style. Pierre refused to let Jean give him anything more than a trim or a 'quick tidy up' and there were only so many questions you could fit into the time it took to do that.

But none of those men were there when Alfred approached Jean's shop that afternoon. Instead he saw a man he didn't recognise sitting in the barber's chair in the window.

'Bonjour Monsieur Neville,' chirped Alfred, as he hopped up the two stone steps and stood in the doorway.

'Alfred. Good to see you. Sit there for a minute, lad, while I finish with this customer.' Jean gestured towards a stool in the corner behind the door, then returned to his work, snipping away in silence.

Alfred did as he was told, and sat crossing and uncrossing his feet as he watched Jean work. He didn't seem quite himself. He was normally so relaxed and jolly. Alfred wondered who the strange man was to have such an unnerving effect on his friend.

Not wanting to stare, Alfred pretended to watch the passers-by out in the street, but as he turned his gaze to the window, he stole a glance at the man's reflection in the mirror. He had to stifle a gasp, for his eyes were drawn instantly to the angry red weal down the side of the man's face. No, this man was definitely not from Oradour. Even without the scar, Alfred would have remembered that hard, narrow face, with its rather angular nose and tiny, bead-like eyes staring intensely straight ahead into the mirror. The man reminded him of a shrew he had seen the other day in the woods.

Just then, Jean finished his work and, nodding politely to his client, whipped the towel away from around his neck and took a step back. The man stood and Alfred saw that he was only small, but his wiry frame suggested he was fit and strong, like an athlete. When he had dusted himself off, the man offered his thanks, paid and promptly left, hurrying off up the street where he climbed into the passenger seat of a delivery van. Alfred stood up and peered out of the door but the van pulled away before he could see if there was anything written on the side.

'Who was that?' he asked Jean, who was rapidly sweeping up the hair from around the base of the chair, as if keen to get rid of all traces of the visitor.

'I don't know,' said Jean, with an edge to his voice that Alfred had never heard before. 'He's not from round here, and take my advice, son, there are times when it's best not to ask.'

'Funny, though,' said Alfred. 'He must have been in Oradour for some kind of business or another. You wouldn't just come here for a haircut, would you?'

'I wouldn't lose any sleep over it, Alfie,' said Jean and, as if anxious to change the subject, he handed him the soap mug and a brush. 'Here, whip me up a good lather. I've got the Mayor coming in any time now and you know how he likes a clean, close shave.'

The Mayor of Oradour, Henri Depaul, was well liked and greatly respected in the village. He still lived in the house overlooking the village green – an open space known locally as the *Champ de Foire* or fairground – in which he had been born seventy-one years ago, and his family's history in Oradour went back generations. Everyone always knew that Henri would be a leading light in the local community. Bright and keen to learn, he had been top of his class right through school and although he had gone away to university in Paris, he wasn't able to break his ties with his home village for long and soon returned to make his life – and find a wife – in Oradour.

Alfred liked Henri Depaul. To him, this well-built, impressive figure of a man, always smartly dressed, with his white hair and frothy white handlebar moustache, represented all that was good about Oradour. He knew everyone in the village and encouraged them all to be good neighbours to one another. He believed in leading by example, and was always polite and well-spoken. Alfred loved the way he walked the entire length and breadth of the village at least once a day, as if checking all was well and to his liking.

Having said that, Alfred had never crossed Henri Depaul and nor would he like to. Everyone at school said that he had no time for anyone who misbehaved or broke the law. But Alfred quite liked the fact that you knew where you were with him. Alfred couldn't imagine the Mayor ever being pushed around. He was like the glue which held the village together. He made Alfred feel safe.

Leaving the barber with a frothy pot of soap for the Mayor's shave, Alfred bid him farewell. He was sure he was still in good time for supper, so he decided to drop in at the smithy before heading for home. Monsieur Lefevre, the blacksmith, was shoeing a particularly frisky horse belonging to Monsieur Brun, the mill owner. The horse was magnificent – all muscle and power – and Alfred marvelled at the way the blacksmith managed to work so swiftly and keep a cool head while expertly tapping the nails through the perfectly crafted iron shoes, his sooty face so close to those mighty hooves.

'Time to call it a day,' said Monsieur Lefevre at last, as he led the Brun horse, complete with four shiny new shoes, out of the smithy and past Alfred, who was sitting on top of the fence.

Alfred had become entranced by the warmth and the fiery glow of the red-hot embers in the furnace, and hadn't noticed the passage of time.

'Oh my goodness!' he cried as he jumped down and landed, two feet together, on the straw-covered cobbles. 'I bet I'm late for supper again. Maman will be so cross. I'd better run. *Au revoir*, Monsieur Lefevre. Thanks for letting me watch.'

With one hand holding onto his cap, Alfred flew out of the yard and headed up the lane. His quickest route home was straight up past the Masson barn, past the garage belonging to Patric Depaul, the mayor's youngest son, and straight on past the tram station. If he ran fast, he could do it in five minutes. But just as he sped past Patric Depaul's doorway, he heard a scuffle and felt a scampering at his heels. It was Bobby, Patric's little black and white dog, thrilled to see his favourite playmate running by.

Without stopping, Alfred looked down into the dog's hopeful little face. 'Not today, Bobby. I can't play with you now. I'm late.'

On hearing the boy's voice the dog began to bark happily and, every few feet, jumped up at Alfred's side, nearly tripping him.

'Oh Bobby,' sighed Alfred, coming to a halt. 'You can't come with me. It's supper time and you know Maman won't let you in the house.'

Looking up at Alfred, Bobby started to wag his tail so furiously that the entire back end of his body wiggled from side to side. Alfred's heart melted.

'Oh, just for a few seconds then,' he said, and knelt

down on the cobbled street to tickle the little dog's tummy. Bobby rolled over onto his back, tail still wagging, his tongue lolling out of the side of his mouth as the boy's fingers ruffled his fur.

The pair had become firm friends over the past few months. Patric Depaul's garage was one of Alfred's favourite places in the village. Patric would let him sit in the vehicles he was working on and pretend to drive them, and he was slowly teaching him the names of all the key parts – the manifold, the spark plugs, the cam belt, the chassis. There was even something called 'the big end', which Alfred thought sounded very bizarre.

But what Alfred liked most of all about visiting Patric was sharing his break-time. They would sit in the yard and Patric would give him some of his bread, cheese and milk while he told him a story or two. Alfred would sit and tickle Bobby behind the ears while he listened.

It was Bobby who had first introduced Patric to Alfred. One day he was lying in the entrance to the garage, watching the village folk go about their morning business, when he saw Alfred approaching from the direction of the bakery, heading home after fetching fresh bread for the family breakfast. As Alfred trotted by, absent-mindedly jangling the change in his pocket and with a large baguette tucked under his arm,

Bobby saw his chance. He jumped to his feet, sprinted out of the garage and, before Alfred knew what was happening, lunged, closing his jaws around the end of the crusty loaf.

'Hey!' Alfred had screamed. 'Let go. That's my breakfast!'

Hearing the commotion, Patric dashed out into the street. At the sight of the young red-haired boy and the dog, mid tug-of-war, one either end of a baguette and both too stubborn to let go, he had to stifle a laugh. Then, realising that the boy might not be quite so amused, he gave out a loud, sharp whistle. Instantly, the dog let go, sat down and issued a little whimper, looking sheepishly at his master.

'I'm so sorry, son,' apologised Patric, looking at the now rather battered and soggy baguette dangling from Alfred's hand. 'Bobby can be a bit of a scamp sometimes, but he means no harm. He's only a pup still. He just wants to play. Let me get you another one of those.'

'Thanks,' said Alfred, giving Patric the damaged bread. 'I like dogs, but he gave me a bit of a surprise. I didn't know whether he was friendly or not.' Feeling more confident now, Alfred patted the dog's head. 'Shall I wait here with him and keep him company while you get the bread?'

Patric nodded and laughed. 'That's a good idea. You two can get to know one another. Bobby could do with a new friend. I'm so busy with the garage here I don't get much time to play with him. I'm Patric, by the way.' He held out his hand.

Alfred wiped the remaining crumbs from his fingers and shook hands. 'I'm Alfred, Alfred Fournier, and I'd be happy to come and play with Bobby, now and then. That is, if Papa says it's alright. He works in the bakery actually, so perhaps you can ask him.'

After that Alfred and Bobby became regular playmates. Alfred took the dog for long walks after school and played with him at the garage as often as he could. The pair became so close that, if Alfred hadn't stopped by for a while, Bobby would come looking for him.

Alfred never ceased to be amazed how Bobby could pop up out of nowhere at any time, sometimes in the most unusual and inconvenient places. There was the occasion when Alfred had gone to old Madame Bodin's funeral and Bobby turned up at his side by the grave, bouncing around most inappropriately and full of the joys of spring. The priest hadn't looked too pleased at all. Then there was the school sports day, when Alfred was playing in the football team and Bobby ran right over the pitch and across the goal mouth to reach him.

Monsieur Gravois, the schoolmaster, had promptly sent Alfred off and kept him on the reserve team for the rest of the term. In fact, wherever Alfred went in Oradour, it was likely that, before long, he would hear the sound of four faithful feet coming up behind him, feel a wet nose on his hand and look down to see Bobby sitting there, tail wagging, looking pleased with himself.

By the time Alfred finally got home that evening, Sylvie was convinced that something dreadful had happened. Both of his elder sisters, Christelle and Sabine, had been sent out to find him, but neither had seen him in the blacksmith's yard so they had returned with no reassuring news. They were debating whether or not to fetch Papa from the bakery when Alfred flew in through the kitchen door, puffing and panting. He took one look at his mother's face as she stood by the stove trying to salvage her fish stew, and knew he had gone too far this time.

'I'm so sorry, Maman. I was at Monsieur Lefevre's. He was shoeing this great big stallion. It was amazing. I lost track of time.'

At first Sylvie didn't say a word. Alfred had to wait while she carefully placed the steaming pot of spoiled supper in the middle of the table. He noticed that her hands were trembling slightly. Then she raised her eyes to meet Alfred's and spoke to him, clearly, slowly and quietly. Alfred was left in no doubt that she meant every single word.

'You will *never* be this late again, Alfred Fournier. From now on, the only explanation I will accept for you not being home on time is that the Germans really *have* come to Oradour. Do you understand? And even if that did happen, we would still know exactly where to find you and that's in those woods behind the cemetery like we agreed. Is that absolutely clear?'

Alfred nodded vigorously, tears prickling the backs of his eyes. 'Yes, Maman. I'm really, really sorry.' He threw his arms around Sylvie's waist, burying his face in her apron. 'I didn't mean to worry you,' he sobbed.

'It's all right, Alfie,' said Sylvie, kissing the top of his head. 'I know you didn't. But I can't bear the thought of anything happening to you. Now sit down and eat your supper.'

As Alfred ate his meal quietly he thought about what his mother had said and how upset she had been. He knew he had hurt one of the people he loved most in the world and he never, ever wanted to do that again.

PART 2

SATURDAY 10 JUNE, 1944 (MORNING)

4: THE SEARCH

MAJOR GENERAL Karl Scholz was not a happy man. He had been woken from a deep sleep in the early hours by a telephone call from one of his soldiers. Some papers had been found in a side street in the city. It was almost certain that they belonged to Major Klausner.

At the mention of his colleague's name, Scholz had sat bolt upright. He had only snatched three hours of sleep but he was instantly wide awake.

'Bring those papers to my office immediately,' he had ordered. 'I want to see them. I'll be there in fifteen minutes.'

If these were indeed Klausner's papers, they could be a vital clue to his whereabouts.

Before heading back to his quarters in Limoges, well after midnight, for some badly-needed rest, Scholz had left strict orders for the search to continue throughout the night. It was clear that Klausner had been the victim of an ambush. His abandoned car, the location in the woods, the tyre tracks. It was classic Resistance. And the more time that passed, the harder the kidnappers would be to trace. Scholz's men had been combing the countryside between the garrison at Guéret and the outskirts of Limoges, but there was so much distance to cover and so many small farm buildings in which the captors could be hiding, it was like looking for a needle in a haystack.

Stressed and troubled, Scholz had tossed and turned before finally falling into an exhausted sleep.

By the time he reached his office, the soldier who had telephoned was already sitting in the chair in front of Scholz's large, imposing desk. He leapt to his feet when Scholz entered, clipped his heels together and raised his arm.

'Heil Hitler.'

Scholz returned the salute. Then, without sitting down, he got straight down to business.

'The papers.'

'Here, Major General. I found them in the gutter. I nearly missed them actually. I thought it was just a piece of litter, but then I noticed the insignia.' He paused while Scholz inspected the now rather damp, creased papers. He could tell by the anguished look which came over the Major General's face that the papers were genuine. Quietly he asked, 'How do you think they got there, Major General?'

'I don't know, but this has got to mean that Major Klausner, or his kidnappers, were in Limoges… and could still be. You searched all the buildings in the street, I take it?'

'Yes, immediately, Major General. But there's nothing to suggest that the kidnappers had any reason to stop there. They could have just been passing through, or hiding there for a while. It's possible Major Klausner threw his papers out of a moving vehicle.'

Scholz sat down and placed the papers carefully before him on his desk. 'I want to ramp up the search. Major Klausner is one of the best. He was awarded the Knight's Cross of the Iron Cross – he is the bravest man I know. He has done his utmost for Germany and now it's our turn to do our utmost for him. Take all the men you can spare and change the focus of the search. Forget Guéret. Tell everyone that the hunt now centres on Limoges.'

As night turned to dawn, Scholz didn't move from his desk. Each time a negative call came in from a search party, he crossed off another section on a map of Limoges, feeling increasingly frustrated and more and more depressed. He had to find Klausner alive. He was far too high a prize for the Resistance to win. The fall-out of this could be huge, for the whole German army as well as for him personally. This had happened on his watch, and just after he had received General Müller's new 'Order of the Day' outlining the latest SS position on the Resistance. In order for the German troops to move north to Normandy without further disruption, it had said, firm reprisals were to be taken against any civilian creating disorder.

And here he was, chasing wildly after one such guerrilla band which continued to outwit his SS troops, right here on his own doorstep. If he let anything happen to Klausner, General Müller would have his head. He *had* to find the abductors and their hostage – sooner rather than later.

Scholz shuddered as he drained the cup of coffee on his desk. He would never get used to that disgusting chicory flavour, and besides, the drink had gone stone cold. God, how he needed some sleep. His eyes were gritty and his head felt like it was packed with cotton wool. He put his head in his hands, desperately trying to stay calm and think clearly. Where in Limoges would he hide if he had kidnapped a top-ranking SS commander?

The loud ringing of the telephone startled him. It was his receptionist.

'There's a Major Heinz Goth here to see you, Major General. He is in a terrible state and looks like he really ought to be in the field hospital. But he says he's got to speak to you. Says it's urgent. He claims to have some vital information in relation to Major Klausner.'

Scholz brightened. 'Send him in at once.'

The man who was shown into Scholz's office was clearly distressed. His left eye was badly swollen, his cheek severely bruised and his bottom lip was split and caked with dried blood. His officer's uniform was filthy and dishevelled, one sleeve torn at the shoulder seam. He swayed as he gave the necessary salute.

'You may sit,' said Scholz, afraid that if he did not give the order the man would collapse on the floor before he had divulged what he knew. 'Tell me who you are. Why are you here?'

The Major sank into the chair and gripped its two arms with his soiled hands, steadying himself. Scholz noticed that the little finger on his right hand was bent horribly sideways, clearly broken.

'I am Storm Leader Heinz Goth,' said the officer, breathing heavily, 'and last night I was kidnapped by the Resistance.'

For a moment, Scholz remained silent as the officer's revelation sank into his fatigued brain. Then he blinked and sat forward sharply, his eyes suddenly alight.

'Go on,' he said.

Goth described how he had been ordered to lead a small party north-west from Limoges to the town of Nieul. They had been instructed to prepare quarters for an assault-gun battalion which was soon to arrive there on its march north to Normandy.

'There were six of us,' he explained, 'in three cars. I was in the lead car with my driver. We'd been warned about the Resistance fighters in the area so we intended to stick together but... I don't know... our car must have been quicker because after a while my driver and I realised we'd lost the others. We must have been going too fast for them to keep up.'

Goth cleared his throat then continued. 'We waited a few minutes but they didn't show. So I told my driver to turn back. We'd gone about a kilometre along the road when we had to stop. A lorry had blocked the road.'

'Why on earth would you stop, man?' Scholz asked, incredulous. 'Didn't you suspect an ambush?'

'The two men who got out were wearing German

uniforms, Major General. We thought they were friends. And besides, we were armed. I had a sub-machine gun.'

As he recalled the scene, Goth's head dropped with shame.

'But I never got to use it. Before we knew it, seven or eight more uniformed men jumped out of the lorry and their weapons were aimed right at us. To go for my gun then would have been suicide. They dragged us out of the car. They kicked and punched us and tore off our uniforms. All we had on was our underwear.'

As he spoke these last few words, Goth's voice cracked and he had to swallow hard before he could carry on. Scholz stifled the urge to hurry him.

'They pushed us off the road into a thicket. I thought that was the end. I was convinced they were going to shoot us there and then. So I did all I could. I offered them a trade. My life for information.'

'My God, what did you tell them?' cried Scholz, a look of panic in his eyes.

'Nothing,' Goth replied quickly. 'I bluffed. I said I could give them some top secret information but I would only share it with their leader. Whoever was at the very top. I was hoping to buy time.'

'So what happened then?' asked Scholz, impatiently.

'We were dragged over to the lorry and told to climb in. They threw our uniforms in after us and drove off.

We got our uniforms back on and I tried to look out for some signs so I could get my bearings. At one point I definitely saw a sign for Oradour.'

Scholz scribbled on his notepad.

'I am not sure which way we went after that but when we next stopped we were in an opening in a forest and there was another lorry there. A French lorry. I could see the tricolour. We were dragged out into the middle of the clearing. Then a man got out of the other lorry, wearing a blue uniform. I assumed he was the leader. I was desperately trying to think what false information I could feed him which would be powerful enough to convince him to let us go.'

'And?' demanded Scholz.

'I didn't get a chance to say anything. The leader started shouting insults at us, calling us SS pigs and telling us we were finished. One of the men who ambushed us kept saying something to him in French. I couldn't understand it but I could tell the leader wasn't pleased. He was yelling at him, as if giving him orders. That was when they led us into the woods.'

Goth looked Scholz directly in the eye. 'They were going to shoot us.'

He paused, but as Scholz didn't speak, he continued.

'My driver realised what was going on and started to struggle. This seemed to infuriate the gang and they set about him, shoving him to the ground and kicking him over and over again. That was when I took my chance and dashed into the trees. I ran for my life.'

'Do you know what happened to your driver?' asked Scholz.

'I heard shots and as I turned round I saw him slump to the ground. There was nothing I could do for him. So I just kept running, looking for cover. They chased me and I could hear them shouting behind me. Shots whistled past my head but I kept changing direction. It was getting dark by then, too, which helped. I could tell I was starting to lose them.'

Goth wiped his eyes with the sleeve of his jacket. 'I came to a railway line and decided to follow it. I knew it had to be the line to Limoges, and I had to make a snap decision about which way to go. Thankfully, I picked the right direction. I walked through the night and didn't stop until I got here. And that was when I heard about Major Klausner's disappearance. I think the same thing could have happened to him. That's why I came straight to you, Major General.'

Scholz sat motionless, taking in the horror of what he had been told.

This was not good news for Klausner. Could it be that the Resistance had executed him already? He could only hope that Klausner's exceptional rank and reputation might make a difference. If the Resistance wanted a bargaining chip, then they had hit the jackpot.

Yes, surely he was more valuable to them alive. Until he heard otherwise, the hunt for Klausner would continue to be a search and rescue mission. And the SS had better be willing to negotiate, humiliating or not. It could be the only way to keep Klausner alive.

He looked at the shattered commander before him. 'You are to be commended for your bravery and for your speed of action. This information is, indeed, crucial in our search for Major Klausner and you can be assured that I will act upon it without delay. For now, you have my thanks.'

Following Scholz's lead, Goth stood and saluted his superior. 'Thank you, Major General.'

'I believe you have earned yourself a good rest,' said Scholz, then inclined his head in the direction of Goth's mangled hand. 'But not, I suggest, before you get those wounds seen to.'

Scholz did not watch as the weary officer limped out of his office. He was already intently studying his map, and he was looking for one place in particular, the place name that Goth had said he had seen on the road sign while in the back of the lorry – Oradour.

As he scanned the area around Goth's known route, his index finger moved across the smooth surface of the map. In no time at all, it came to rest on Oradour, directly west from Nieul – Goth's original destination. After checking the scale of the map, he set his compass to draw a circle with a radius of twenty kilometres and jabbed the pin into Oradour. The result was as he suspected: Nieul sat well within the circle. Goth's account was accurate. The forest where he had been taken by his captors could well have been close to Oradour.

But this wasn't what struck Scholz most. His eyes kept being drawn to the south-east portion of the circle, which took in the outskirts of Limoges. The circle encompassed the very same suburb in which Klausner's papers had been found, and leading out from there was a good, fast road, leading all the way to Oradour. On a quiet night, it was a distance a car could cover in no more than twenty minutes.

Scholz sat back in his chair and chewed on his lip as he firmed up his next move in his mind. He now had a new field of search. He would give the order to begin searching all the buildings and the wooded areas within a narrow corridor following that route out of Limoges, ending at Oradour.

5: THE ORDERS

MAJOR GUSTAV Dietrich arrived with his battalion at the barracks in Rouchehout, ten kilometres south-west of Saint Junien, feeling every one of his twenty-nine years. Their march north to Normandy had not begun well and repeated attacks from the Resistance, including the two in close succession as they crossed the Dordogne River, had taken their toll. The men had been on the move for days, snatching only a few hours' sleep here and there. They were exhausted and hungry, and Dietrich was finding it difficult to keep their spirits up with the prospect of at least another four hard days of travel ahead.

Dietrich was anxious to make up some of the time they had lost thanks to the Resistance, but he knew that to push his men on, before they had had time to rest and recover, would be counterproductive. Many of them were nursing injuries from the attacks and, as some of the battalion's vehicles had been damaged beyond repair, there were others who had been forced to complete the route on foot and who were suffering from badly blistered feet.

So although it was early morning, Dietrich sent his men to their bunks and would have gladly headed straight for his own quarters had he not been waylaid by a messenger claiming to have crucial intelligence from a French informant. Dietrich was so shocked by what he heard that he immediately summoned his driver. He had to get to Limoges, he yelled, and he had to get there fast.

The warm morning sun did nothing to lift Dietrich's mood as he arrived outside Scholz's command centre in Limoges.

'Wait here,' he barked at his driver, Ragnar, as he straightened his hat. 'This won't take long.'

Dietrich sprinted into the building, his long legs making light of the steep stone steps. Once in the marble hallway, he strode over to the young receptionist who was busy sending a telegram, and tapped sharply on her desk with his cane. The girl jumped and looked up at him wide-eyed.

'Major Gustav Dietrich. Here to see Major General Scholz.'

Although offended by Dietrich's abrupt manner,

the young girl was taken aback by his good looks and her hand hovered over the telephone, momentarily paralysed. She couldn't drag her eyes away from his face, its features so finely chiselled, the nose so strong, his complexion smooth and sun-bronzed and his eyes a piercing blue.

'I suggest you dial Major General Scholz's number fast,' said Dietrich sarcastically, 'unless you want the blood of a top SS commander on your hands!'

'Of course. Sorry, Major.' The girl's hand trembled as she dialled her boss's extension. When she spoke into the receiver she dropped her eyes to her notepad, avoiding the compelling gaze of the man before her. She felt that if she looked at him, he would be able to see right into her soul.

'There's a… a Major Gustav Dietrich to see you, Major General,' she stammered. 'Yes, yes, of course. You can go straight in, Major,' she said quickly, but when she looked up, Dietrich had already turned his back to her and was striding purposefully towards Scholz's door.

'I have an extremely distressing report from one of my informants,' Dietrich announced, removing his gloves to reveal long, slender fingers, then folding them confidently on his knee. 'A German commander, a high-ranking SS commander, has been kidnapped by the Resistance and is being held captive somewhere between here and Saint Junien.'

Dietrich raised his chin and sat back in the chair, clearly expecting this revelation to be met with a strong reaction from his superior.

'Yes, we are well aware of that,' said Scholz, bristling at Dietrich's over-confident manner. Dietrich had burst into his office and sat down with only the briefest of salutes. He was obviously a man with a very high opinion of himself.

'You appear to be a little behind on the news around here,' he added, watching Dietrich closely and enjoying the look of disappointment in his eyes. 'That's understandable, of course. I am aware that the Resistance has been keeping you busy, too, and of course you are to be congratulated on getting your battalion this far with so few losses. But I can assure you that the search for Major Klausner is well in hand also.'

Scholz didn't foresee the impact that the mention of Klausner's name would have on Dietrich. The blood instantly drained from the Major's face and his hands clenched into fists, the knuckles white.

'They have taken Klausner? Major Thomas Klausner?'

'Yes,' said Scholz, taken aback. 'But I can assure you that we are doing everything we can to find him and, as soon as he's safe, we'll eliminate his abductors.'

Dietrich stood up and began pacing back and forth across the thin strip of red carpet in front of Scholz's desk, twisting his gloves in his hands.

'You know him personally?' asked Scholz, cautiously, unnerved by the reaction he was witnessing.

'We served together on the Eastern front. He is one of the best men I know. One of the bravest. Most decorated. And yes, I am proud to call him a friend. This can't be happening!'

The antagonism Scholz originally felt for Dietrich began to subside. 'Trust me, we've been throwing everything at the situation. All through the night. All the men I have at my disposal. And we're closing in. We've now narrowed the search to a strip of countryside between the outskirts of Limoges and a village called Oradour.'

Scholz dropped his gaze. 'It's a little humiliating, I know, but I have ordered the search parties to take white flags with them.'

Dietrich stopped pacing. 'White flags?' he asked incredulously.

'Well,' replied Scholz, feeling obliged to justify his decision, 'even if we aren't willing to negotiate, we may need the Resistance to think that we are. It might be the only way to get Klausner out alive.'

Dietrich placed both hands on Scholz's desk, looking him straight in the eye. 'But don't you realise, it could be too late?' he said, through gritted teeth.

'I don't believe the Resistance will shoot him, if that's what you mean,' said Scholz. 'He's too valuable.'

'No, they won't shoot him,' cried Dietrich, leaning aggressively towards Scholz across the desk, 'because they intend to burn him alive!'

Scholz shrank back. 'Good God, man, what makes you think that?'

'A French informant makes me think that. It's going to be quite a ceremony, I believe,' spat Dietrich. 'And why wouldn't they burn him? They've caught one of the highest-ranking SS officers they could possibly find. They want to send a message – a warning – to us all, and they want to make sure that we listen!'

'I think you'd better sit down,' Scholz said firmly.

Reluctantly, Dietrich sat, shaking his head at Scholz's apparent naivety.

'Look, even if you're right, we may still have time,' continued Scholz. 'The Resistance will want to make sure their actions have the biggest impact. And they can't move Klausner far, we have men swarming like bees over the whole area between here and Oradour.'

Dietrich sat forward in the chair, his blue eyes suddenly narrowing. 'Why do you keep mentioning Oradour?' he asked.

Scholz gave Dietrich a summary of Heinz Goth's kidnap and narrow escape and how Goth had seen a sign for Oradour near to the Resistance gang's rendezvous point.

'Then there's no question,' said Dietrich. 'I should go straight to Oradour. I will turn out every house, every building, every barn, until I find something.'

'We don't know for certain that that's where Klausner is being held,' said Scholz, sensing a need to rein in the young commander's enthusiasm. 'There are three other villages in that area that we haven't yet searched. I agree that Oradour is a target for our search, but I will not have you storming in and stirring up more anti-German feeling. We are trying to smother our opposition, not fan the flames. And we have no firm evidence that anyone in Oradour is involved in this. In fact, I'm told that Oradour has always been a peaceful village with no track record of Resistance activity.'

'But it's the best place to start looking,' said Dietrich, 'and you need me to get involved. You need all the help you can get.'

Scholz fought to control his anger at Dietrich's thinly disguised insult. 'Major Dietrich, you have a battalion to lead, and a long way to go before you reach Normandy. I have this under control.'

'Maybe you do,' said Dietrich, 'but you have no one out there in the field of my calibre – no one who can think on their feet and direct the search better than I. Besides, I have to do this for Klausner. I can't let him down.'

Scholz sighed, relenting. He had taken a sound dislike to this arrogant man but he had to admire his persistence.

'Very well,' he agreed. 'But if you're going to get involved it will be on my terms. You will follow my orders. Understand?'

'Yes, sir,' said Dietrich, putting on his gloves. 'So what's the plan?'

'You can take charge of 3rd Company. The Captain is Heinrich Krüger. You can brief him in Saint Junien and assemble the Company there. Looking at the size of the area we have to cover, I'd say you'll need enough vehicles for about a hundred and eighty men.'

Dietrich nodded sharply, eager to get going.

'When you reach Oradour, surround the village. From the map it looks like it's a relatively easy place to seal off but you've got time to study the road layout on your way back to Saint Junien. I think there are just four routes in and out. Oh, and there's a tram line, so

61

you'll need to get some men posted at the tram station once you're inside.'

Scholz paused and looked Dietrich in the eyes. 'My orders are that you search the village from top to bottom – but do it carefully. I don't want any panic. Tell the villagers that it's a standard search, that you just want to see their identity papers. But don't leave any stone unturned. If Klausner is there, or there is any trace of him having been there, I want to know.'

'And if I find nothing?' asked Dietrich.

'Then you move out,' answered Scholz, slightly puzzled. 'Report back to me and await my next orders. By then we might have located Klausner elsewhere. As I said, there is no guarantee that the kidnappers have any connection with Oradour.'

'But there is another option,' said Dietrich, a conspiratorial smile on his lips. 'To ensure that our time is not completely wasted.'

'And that would be?' asked Scholz, warily.

'I take hostages,' said Dietrich. 'As a bargaining tool. Why not play the Resistance at their own game?'

Scholz sucked in his cheeks. He didn't like the idea of taking civilians hostage. There had been too many cases under the leadership of General Müller where so-called hostages had ended up dead. Scholz was certain that Müller had never intended to use them for negotiation. But he couldn't deny that there was logic in Dietrich's idea – and if all their searches for Klausner proved futile, they would need a back-up plan.

Dietrich was looking at him keenly, his blond eyebrows raised, willing him to agree.

'Very well. You may take thirty hostages. No more. And they are not to be mistreated, understood? They are to be used to negotiate with the Resistance and for no other purpose. Remember who the enemy is here.'

Scholz felt forced to stress this to Dietrich. He had heard much about this young soldier and his rapid rise through the ranks of the SS. He had an admirable military record but Scholz could also sense a ruthlessness and an impetuosity that made him nervous.

'Is that all absolutely clear?' Scholz asked again as he pushed back his chair and stood, ready to dismiss the young commander.

'Of course,' replied Dietrich, smiling as he rose to salute. 'Get ready to be impressed, Major General.'

6: GUSTAV DIETRICH

GUSTAV HERBERT Dietrich was born at home in Freiburg in the early hours of a raw, frost-covered December day in 1914. A handsome and healthy-looking baby, with a mass of thick, dark hair, the newborn Gustav instantly invaded his mother's heart and aroused such love and devotion that, as she kissed the long slender fingers on his tiny hands for the very first time, she swore that she would never love anyone as much as he. She knew that whatever this child did in his life, she would love and support him… and she would forgive him anything.

To his father, the new baby was a triumph, the culmination of years of hope. Life was now as it should be and he had regained control of his destiny.

Otto and Klara Dietrich had been trying for a baby ever since they married ten years before. Confused as to why God refused to grant her the one thing she wanted most in her life, Klara had suffered with recurring bouts of deep depression, during which she would retreat to her room for days, unable to face the world.

At first, Otto sympathised with his wife in her anguish. He gave her the time she needed to work her way back from the darkness of her despair. But as the years went by, and no baby came, Otto grew resentful of Klara's moods and found it harder to hide his impatience. He was tired of trying, weary of keeping up the pretence that all was well in the Dietrich household. His teaching career was blossoming, he had his sights on a headship at the boys' school where he worked in Freiburg, and he needed a strong wife by his side.

As the country moved dangerously towards war, Otto and Klara enjoyed a degree of shelter from the growing unease that was spreading around their city. As a teacher, Otto's civilian post was secure, and in the autumn of 1913, his career ambition was fulfilled when he was appointed headmaster. Meanwhile Klara, now approaching thirty, finally seemed to be coming to terms with the prospect of life without motherhood. Her tendency to depression seemed to be lifting and the atmosphere in the Dietrich home was noticeably more cheerful and relaxed.

Perhaps it was because the couple no longer obsessed over the idea of becoming parents; perhaps it was because Klara was happier; perhaps it was just fate. The cause didn't matter to the Dietrichs. What did matter was that the spring of 1914 brought with it the promise of new life. Klara discovered that she was, at last, expecting a child.

As if sensing how long his parents had longed for his arrival, little Gustav seemed determined, right from the start, not to let them down. Even as a toddler, all he wanted to do was please Otto and Klara, and he would cry huge tears whenever his father found reason to scold him.

Although he loved his son, Otto was an academic to the core and he treated every day of Gustav's life like an educational challenge. Every game, every play-time had a learning purpose, every meal was analysed for its nutritional value, every conversation was carefully structured, and every family day out was meticulously planned so that Gustav would return with his head full of facts.

'He's not one of your pupils, Otto, he's your son,' Klara remarked one day, as she heard him correcting Gustav's grammar during what should have been a casual conversation over breakfast.

'That may be the case, my dear,' Otto replied, rather pompously, 'but children's brains are like sponges and it's my duty to fill them up. If I can't teach my own son properly, then what does that say about me?'

Klara didn't answer.

'Mark my words, Gustav is going to be the brightest boy in his class when he goes to school.'

In contrast to Otto's rather austere, formal parenting style, Klara's approach was to smother the boy with love. She was constantly kissing and cuddling him, tickling him and playing silly games. She would sing to him all the time and snuggle up next to him at bedtime to tell him stories at night. Gustav had become her world and she devoted her days to his happiness.

'You spoil that boy,' Otto would tell her. 'You will make him too soft. He needs more discipline. A tougher backbone and a bit more male company wouldn't hurt him either.'

Klara wouldn't argue with her husband, but nor would she listen to him. She disliked her husband's strict, hands-off, businesslike approach to bringing up their son and was determined to make Gustav feel wanted and loved. So, even when he was in trouble with Otto, she would find a way to sneak him a cuddle, a kiss or a piece of gingerbread to help soothe his tears.

But as Gustav grew older, reaching school age, Klara began to notice that all her warmth and outward displays of love were still not enough for her son. She could tell that Gustav craved a real demonstration of affection from his father. She sensed how deeply felt Otto's reprimands were, and she knew that all Gustav wanted to do was please him.

When she lay awake at night, listening to Otto's gentle breathing, she would turn and look into his face and will him to wake up the next morning and be proud of his son and love him for who he was.

Klara never knew whether Gustav managed to make his father proud, for one day, not long after Gustav's ninth birthday, she collapsed while clearing the snow from the steps on the back porch.

When the doctor had been and gone, Otto tried to explain to a dazed Gustav why nothing could have been done to stop the bleeding inside Klara's head.

'She wasn't scared, Gustav,' he said, as he looked down at his son sitting in a state of shock halfway up the stairs. 'It was so quick. Like switching out a light really. They call it a haemorrhage. These things can just happen, without much warning.'

Even when his own heart was breaking, Otto offered his son no embrace, no strong arm around the shoulders, no shared tears. Only an awkward hand placed stiffly on his knee, and a moment's pause, before mumbling about needing to make the 'necessary arrangements'.

He felt sorry for the poor lad, but sentimentality had never suited him terribly well. Otto always kept his emotions under control, locked deep inside him, as if in a secret safe inside his heart, and it was to here that he now banished the strangling grief caused by the loss of his beloved Klara. He was terrified that if he dared open that safe door, even just a tiny crack, in order to let Gustav in, he would never regain control.

In bed that night, Gustav sobbed into his pillow. His father had been so brave all day and he didn't want to let him down by being a crybaby. But he couldn't hold back the tears any longer. He felt so alone, so completely lost. He ached for his mother, her gentleness, her kindness and her soothing words. If she were here now, he thought, she would stroke his hair and tell him everything was going to be alright.

Gustav knew that life would be very different from that point on, now it was just Father and him. His mother's death had left such a huge void in their lives, and Gustav was certain that his mother would have wanted him to try and fill that void with love. But to get close to his father, Gustav believed he had to rid himself of all the weaknesses he knew Otto saw in him.

If he was too emotional, too sensitive, he would become more of a man and join the football team, learn how to box or take up hunting. And if he was too slow at school, he would concentrate harder in class and spend longer on his homework.

One way or another, he would make his father proud.

By the time he reached his teenage years, Gustav had succeeded in burying the soft and gentle side of his character. Now long-limbed and athletic, he started to discover that he had a natural talent for most physical activities, and because he was good at the sports he played, he was more often than not chosen to lead the team. Having his talents acknowledged, and seeing his team-mates so willing to put their trust in him, was like a shot in the arm to Gustav and he quickly became addicted to this new sense of power and authority.

Out of school, he joined a shooting club, and rapidly became his instructor's favourite. He was quick to learn how to handle a gun and proved himself to have a sharp eye and a steady hand. To hone his new talent, Gustav saved up his pocket money and bought a second-hand air rifle and after that spent hours on his own in the woods near his home, shooting at rabbits, birds and squirrels. He never took any of his kills home, nor told anyone how many creatures he had hit, but he kept a secret tally in a little notebook in his jacket pocket, and each month set himself a new target to beat.

But Gustav's sporting successes seemed to count for little in his father's eyes. What mattered most to Otto was education and academic achievement, and in that Gustav simply could not excel. No matter how much effort he put in, his school results were always disappointing, always lower than average.

At first, his father blamed the teachers, and took it upon himself to give Gustav extra tuition. But as time went on and Gustav's results fell further and further below average, Otto's disappointment became tinged with embarrassment. That was when the snide remarks began, the little jokes and quips about Gustav's lack of intelligence and prospects, which gradually gnawed away at his self-confidence.

Matters came to a head when Gustav came home from secondary school one day to break the news to his father that his teachers wanted him to repeat his sixth year.

Appalled, Otto struck out, using the one weapon that could cause Gustav greater pain than any fist, strap or belt. 'You are pathetic,' he said, sneering at his son across the dining table. 'How can you be my offspring? I am headmaster of the top boys' school in Freiburg and yet I have a son who has little more intelligence than a slug. It's a good thing that your mother didn't live to see this day. She would have been so ashamed.'

After that, the distance between father and son grew day by day. Conversation was reduced to short, clipped exchanges over dinner, after which Otto would withdraw to his office to work, staying there until long after Gustav had gone to bed.

In trying to shut out the pain of his wife's death, Otto had locked away any tenderness he once had for his son, until he was unable to express anything but bitterness and resentment. It was if he saw Gustav as the cause of everything that had gone wrong in his life, all of which seemed beyond his control, and all his son could offer him in payment for that was disappointment and humiliation.

Lonely, rejected and yet desperate to please, the tall, gangly, teenage Gustav was an eager recruit for the National Socialist German Workers Party. He had long admired its leader, Adolf Hitler, and was wooed by his promises to improve the German economy with things like tax cuts for farmers and protection of food prices. But more than anything, he wanted to belong to something, to feel accepted and to be among people who were like-minded. He felt sure that the Nazi party could offer him all those things – as well as an escape route from his stifling life in Freiburg.

Gustav had no intention of jumping too soon. The Nazis were battling for power with the Communists.

Their violent methods had lost them both popular support and votes, and Gustav didn't want to ally himself with a losing side. But after the elections of November 1932, when the 43-year-old Hitler was made Germany's new Chancellor, Gustav knew that the time was right. Finally he could see a way out, he could leave his traumatic school life behind him and head for a place where he would be needed and could have a chance to succeed.

Now a tall, athletic, handsome and imposing figure, the 19-year-old Gustav immediately made a good impression. He was loyal and eager to please and was quick to volunteer for Work Service in Naumburg. While there he applied to join the Special Forces and by 1936 he had been called up to the SS Signals Battalion in Berlin.

Gustav continued to impress his superiors, thriving within an atmosphere, so alien to him and yet so welcome, in which good effort and attitude was rewarded with praise and recognition.

A year later, Gustav was sent to the SS Officers' School in Bad Tölz where he became an SS Cadet Officer. It took him only four and a half months to complete a platoon leader's course, and his hard work was repaid with a promotion to SS Upper Cadet Officer in the Germania Regiment.

Another step up, to 2nd Lieutenant, followed later that year and, alongside his men, Gustav proudly marched into the Sudetenland, along the mountainous borders of Czechoslovakia, a strategically important area which had been signed over to Germany by Britain, Italy and France through the Munich Agreement.

'My leadership skills have been well recognised,' Gustav wrote in a letter to his father. 'After leaving the Sudetenland I was instructed to lead a platoon to the Polish front. We had a successful campaign with minimal losses and Herr Hitler saw fit to award me the Iron Cross 2nd Class. Thanks to that I have now been appointed Adjutant of the 2nd Company of the SS Regiment "Germania" which I hope makes you proud.

'I think of you often, Father, and it is my dearest wish that the news I send of my faithful service to our beloved Nazi Germany brings you some comfort and peace of mind.'

Far from the battlefield, surrounded by books and papers in his study, Otto found it difficult to identify with the experiences his son described in his letters. The ranks, titles and awards he listed meant nothing to him and so his replies to Gustav were brief and to the point.

In May 1940, Otto received another letter from Gustav, who he knew had been fighting in Northern

France. This time, when he saw the Military Hospital letterhead, his heart stopped. His hand shook as he read, fearing the worst.

'I am in bad shape, Father,' Gustav wrote. 'A serious gunshot wound to the lungs. The damned French nearly got me. The doctors tell me that it's a miracle I survived. But here I still am. I am feeling pretty rough, though, and am finding being incapacitated extremely difficult. It looks as though I shall be convalescing here for a while yet, so if you should find the time to write to me, I would dearly like to hear about life in Freiburg. The house, you, it all seems so far away now. Do write to tell me how you are. Your ever loving son, Gustav.'

Every night, as Gustav lay in his hospital bed, the same nightmare scene crept into his slumber. He saw himself running through the thick mud, shouting to his men to give him cover. Then came the dull thud. The searing pain in his chest… and then the sensation of the cold, oozing mud on his hands, mixing with his own blood as he lay there, struggling to breathe, on the battlefield. As his chest tightened to bursting point, he saw the same, familiar figure standing in the distance. A man, wearing civilian clothes, a grey woollen suit and tie, staring at him amid all the chaos of the fighting. Gustav stretched out his hand, but the figure always turned away, fading into the fog.

Gustav was discharged from the Military Hospital three months later. During the long and tedious weeks he had spent there recovering, he had received his highest award for bravery, the Iron Cross 1st Class, and a promotion to Battalion Commander – but no letter from his father.

7: THE BRIEFING

THE DRIVE from Limoges back to Saint Junien couldn't pass by quickly enough for Gustav Dietrich. Before he had left Scholz's offices he had asked the girl on reception to get the leader of 3rd Company on the telephone so he could assemble the key officers for a briefing. They were to meet at the Hotel de la Gare at eleven o'clock sharp.

What a stupid girl that receptionist was! It was painful watching her fumbling away trying to dial the number, and when she started stammering into the phone Dietrich couldn't bear it any longer. Glaring, he had snatched the handset from her and impatiently ushered her away.

Besides, he needed to contact his French informants, too. It was essential that they were at the briefing to share the latest intelligence on Resistance activity and, hopefully, Klausner's whereabouts.

Calls made, Dietrich had marched out of the building

and jumped back into his car, instructing Ragnar, his driver, to get him back to St Junien without delay.

Ragnar was used to following Major Dietrich's orders. He had been Dietrich's personal assistant ever since he became Battalion Commander and he wasn't going to put such a cushy job into jeopardy by seeming unhelpful or incompetent. Ragnar had worked hard to build a good working relationship with Dietrich, which wasn't easy. The Major was a volatile, unpredictable man. You never knew what he would do next. Ragnar did not like him one jot, but he knew what happened to people who got on the wrong side of Major Gustav Dietrich so he was never going to let him know his true feelings towards him. No, he was too smart for that, and Dietrich trusted him.

Ragnar could see that Dietrich's meeting with Major General Scholz had gone well. Dietrich had a look of smug satisfaction on his face as he sat in the back seat of the car.

'Everything all right, Major?' he asked his boss as they sped along the main road out of Limoges.

'If you call having to pick up the pieces of a shambles of a mission to find a top SS officer all right, then yes, I guess it is!' remarked Dietrich sarcastically. He always felt he could let off steam with Ragnar. Whatever he said to him stayed with him. 'You know, this hostage situation is a whole lot worse than I thought. They've taken Major Klausner, Thomas Klausner, and they intend to execute him – and that cretin of a Major General in there is bumbling about without a clue. It's no surprise that the Resistance are running rings around us with snails like that in charge.'

Meeting Dietrich's steely gaze in his rear view mirror, Ragnar shook his head in sympathetic exasperation and frowned.

Dietrich went on, 'But I'm in charge now. I'm going to start shaking the beehive, starting with Oradour.'

They arrived at the Hotel de la Gare just before eleven o'clock. Ragnar parked outside and waited in the car at the bottom of the hotel steps, rolling down his window to let in some air. The sun was now rising higher in the sky and it promised to be a very warm afternoon. He lit a cigarette and gazed up at the façade of the hotel. The pale blue painted shutters on the windows were all closed, and Ragnar tried to imagine what heated debate was going on inside the cool, dark rooms.

Dietrich was meeting with the Captain of the 3rd Company, Heinrich Krüger, the Gestapo secret police, and some French informants. Ragnar wondered whether the informants had any news of Klausner and, more importantly, if the poor devil was still breathing.

Dietrich had said that the Resistance intended to burn him alive, but Ragnar found that hard to believe. Surely they wouldn't dare do something so horrific to a man like Klausner. They must know what kind of response they would get from the SS.

Ragnar kept an eye on the station clock across the road. He smoked four cigarettes, allowing himself one every quarter of an hour, and was just deciding whether to have a fifth when the front door of the hotel opened. Dietrich and Krüger emerged, and from their body language Ragnar could see that an unfinished argument still raged between them. Dietrich seemed incensed about something, and his whole frame was taut. He took an urgent stride towards the top of the steps but Krüger shot out a hand and caught hold of his arm.

Ragnar could just hear the note of desperation in his voice. 'You can't do this, Commander. It hasn't been sanctioned. Don't lead my men into this.'

Spinning round on his heels, Dietrich looked down at Krüger's hand on his arm, his eyes wide with incredulity, as if Krüger had just injected him with poison. 'You dare challenge my authority?' he seethed. 'I can do this, and I will! Your men are in my command now and they will do whatever I tell them to.'

Krüger dropped his hand to his side and took a step back, defeated. 'I want no part of it,' he said.

'Fine,' snapped Dietrich, turning his back and carrying on down the steps. 'This is a mission for SS men, not lily-livered cowards!'

Krüger's mouth fell open. Stunned into silence, he watched as Dietrich got into his car, his sculpted features set hard as he sat facing straight ahead and barked instructions to his driver. Ragnar saw a look of nausea on Krüger's face, and watched his mouth form the words, 'God help them all,' before he turned slowly and went back inside.

PART 3

SATURDAY 10 JUNE, 1944 (LUNCHTIME)

8: ORADOUR

ALFRED WAS one of the last pupils to take his seat in the noisy, bustling classroom at the School for Lorraine Refugee Children that Saturday morning. Rarely was he keen to get to school (there was always something far more interesting to do besides staying indoors and having boring old lessons with Mr Gravois), but on this particular Saturday he found it especially hard to drag himself through the school gate. It was the day before Corpus Christi, after all, and as many children would be taking Communion for the first time in the Sunday Mass, there was lots of excitement and activity in the village. The residents had been preparing for the festivities for days, appreciating the distraction from the worries and fears that accompanied German occupation.

So even as Alfred trailed behind his sisters, Christelle and Sabine, across the fairground on his way to school, kicking at the early morning dew on the grass, the village was already beginning to buzz with expectation.

The first tram had arrived from Limoges and a crowd of day-trippers scurried past Alfred down the street. A group of elderly men had stepped off first, helping one another to unload their fishing tackle before heading down to the river. Behind them came the ladies from the outlying villages, empty shopping baskets at the ready, eager to stock up on food provisions and beat the rush to find the freshest bread, the fattest sausages, the tastiest preserves, the plumpest apricots, the tangiest goats' cheese or the freshest turnips – and the best of whatever meat was left after the Germans had taken their majority share.

It didn't seem right to Alfred that the French farmers worked so hard yet they had to surrender the cream of their crops. Not only did the Germans demand more than half of all the meat that was produced, they also took a good share of the fruit and vegetables. He would never forget the look of disgust on the face of his friend Monsieur Demarais from the wine store when he revealed to Alfred that the Germans had the nerve to claim eighty per cent of all the champagne that was produced as well. For Monsieur Demarais, that really was an arrow through the heart of French pride.

Like Alfred, the headmaster Monsieur Gravois did not seem happy to be in school that morning.

'Alfred Fournier, if you don't sit down right away and get ready to listen to what I have to say, you will be spending the morning scrubbing the toilet floor,' he yelled, as Alfred ambled into the classroom.

'Sorry, sir,' Alfred mumbled, as he took his place on the end of the row.

Monsieur Gravois explained to the class how they were all going to have to sit and work very quietly that morning and get on with their essays about the fall of the Roman Empire. They would be called out, one by one, he said, to go and see Doctor Depaul for their health check and injection and, as there were so many children to see, including all those who had come into Oradour from the surrounding villages, they would have to come back into school after lunch.

As this last sentence was met by a communal groan from the class, Monsieur Gravois relented.

'I know it's no fun having to come into school on a sunny summer's afternoon, but if you are all well behaved and don't dilly dally when it's your turn to see the doctor,' (at this point he looked directly at Alfred), 'I might let you out for lunch a little early. And those of you who have already seen the doctor by then can have the afternoon off, as it's a special day.'

A cheer went round the room and Alfred felt a little happier as he took out his pencil and exercise book and began to write. Alfred liked history and was fascinated by the stories Monsieur Gravois had told the class about the Romans. He found it hard to believe that, so long ago, they had already invented so many amazing things and built incredible structures like the Colosseum.

But Alfred was also intrigued by the way in which the Romans' great love of art, of beauty and of poetry and literature, was offset by an equally great capacity for cruelty. He wondered if the people who lived in France in the first century BC felt the same about the Romans taking over their land as his family and friends did about the Germans coming.

As he daydreamed about life all those years ago, Alfred stared out of the window down towards the river. The meadow across the road from the school looked as though it was covered in a blanket of snow – in fact, it was a soft, undulating field of white narcissi, flecked here and there with dense pockets of dark purple pansies. On the far side, he could just make out the fishermen he had seen earlier getting off the tram, dotted along the river bank, sitting patiently in the shade of the trees, waiting for a bite. Alfred imagined the pike and the perch darting around the rocks in the crystal clear waters and the carp lurking in the deep pools between the tree roots by the banks. He wished he was out in the fresh air too, and wondered if his friend Monsieur Babin the clog-maker would be able to take him fishing later on, after he had closed up his shop.

Just before noon, Monsieur Gravois let the children go off for their lunch break. Unfortunately for Alfred and his sisters, they were among the group who had not yet been seen by Doctor Depaul.

'If you have had your medical check, you can go home,' said Monsieur Gravois. 'I want the rest of you back here for one o'clock sharp. The sooner we get started again, the sooner you will be free.'

Alfred, Christelle and Sabine walked together in the sunshine up the street towards the fairground, the sound of all the happy lunchtime chatter in the village centre growing louder with each step. This was the Oradour Alfred loved: bursting with life, everyone in high spirits. All the tables outside the street cafés were full of happy customers and the streets were a splash of colour, the perfect setting for tomorrow's procession, lined with tubs of pink and lilac petunias and with waterfalls of red and white geraniums tumbling overhead from dozens of hanging baskets.

At the bakery the children met up with their father, who had just finished his shift. He was bringing home three long baguettes wrapped in brown paper and the delicious smell of the warm, crusty bread made Alfred's stomach rumble. He took his father's hand.

'What've you been learning about in school today, then, Alfie?' his father enquired with a smile.

'The Romans,' said Alfred, 'which is good, 'cause I like them, but I'd still rather be outside playing. And it's not fair. Christelle, Sabine and I and some of the other kids have to go back after lunch as we haven't seen the doctor yet. The others get the afternoon off.'

Just then Alfred saw a long line of men outside the *tabac*. 'Who are they?' he asked, pointing to the queue. He only recognised a couple of the men. The rest must have come into village that day.

'They're queuing for their tobacco rations. How could I have forgotten! Today's tobacco delivery day. I'll come back for mine after lunch. I need to pick up my ration card from home first. Hey, look over there!'

Leon had seen their old friends Ethan and Rachael having lunch on the terrace of the Hotel de la Glane.

'Come on, let's pop over and say hello. I haven't

seen them for a couple of weeks. But don't forget, it's Monsieur and Madam Bonheur now.'

Soon after he and his wife had arrived in Oradour with the Fourniers, Ethan had followed the advice of his brother, Joseph, and had changed their names to Emile and Rochelle Bonheur. Oradour had so far remained a safe bolthole for Jews but there was no sense in advertising their origins.

Ethan and Rachael greeted Leon, Christelle, Sabine and Alfred with warm hugs and kisses. Their traumatic shared journey across France four years previously had been the beginning of a firm friendship between the two families, and the old couple treated the Fournier children like adopted grandchildren.

'Look at you,' Rachael said to Alfred, ruffling his fringe. 'I swear you get at least two centimetres taller every time I see you. Oh, and girls, you must come and see me soon. I have just bought some gorgeous floral fabric from the draper's shop and I would be happy to make you a blouse each from it. I thought of you two when I saw it. The colours are perfect for you.'

Leon noticed Alfred gazing longingly at the mouth-watering roast pike laid out on the big oval platter in between Ethan and Rachael.

'That would be very kind of you, Rach... er, Rochelle,' he said, 'but we mustn't keep you from your meal any longer. The children have to be back at school soon too, so we'd better leave you in peace. We just wanted to say hello.'

As Alfred continued on his way home alongside his father and sisters, he sensed a movement behind him. It was Bobby, eyes shining, bursting with pride at having found his friend amongst the crowds milling around the village centre.

'Hello, boy,' Alfred said softly, crouching to cuddle the little dog. 'You are a clever thing, finding me today. There are so many people here. Fancy a race home?'

Straightening up, Alfred began to jog along the road, laughing out loud as, every couple of metres, the little dog leapt up into the air at his side like a spring lamb.

Behind them, Leon put one arm around each of his daughters' shoulders and smiled. He suddenly felt content. Perhaps his family was finally beginning to move on. Charly, their old life, their eviction, it didn't matter so much any more. What mattered most to him was right here, all around him in this beautiful village, and he realised how lucky they were to have found their way to Oradour, a place where they had friends, a haven of peace amid all the chaos and horror of the war. His family had been given a new chance, a new life and, at that moment, he realised that he would do anything, anything at all, to protect it.

9: THE GATHERING OF THE TROOPS

AS THE station clock opposite the Hotel de la Gare struck one, twenty officers and a hundred and eighty-seven men from 3rd Company began to assemble their convoy, ready to move out of Saint Junien as Dietrich had ordered. The atmosphere as the soldiers gathered around their vehicles was alive with an explosive mix of excitement and trepidation. No one yet knew where they were headed nor why they suddenly found themselves in the command of Major Dietrich rather than their own commanding officer, Captain Krüger, but they had a sense that they were about to be involved in something big.

Major Dietrich had been pacing about intently, rushing up and down the line of vehicles, organising the men, giving out instructions and checking their weapons. Meanwhile, as he waited patiently by the Major's car, his driver Ragnar marvelled at Dietrich's efficiency and focus. Like him or not, he thought, you had to admire the man's dogged determination. He had a clear plan and if to achieve it he had to brush aside someone like Captain Krüger and take over the command of his men, he would do it without batting an eyelid. Dietrich had an undeniable talent for getting people to do what he wanted. With his imposing height, steely gaze and sharp eyes, he seemed to command an instant response from any soldier he spoke to. It had taken only minutes for Dietrich to galvanise the men into action and here they were, an hour after the briefing at the hotel, virtually ready to go.

Most of the soldiers were young, around eighteen to twenty years of age, and many were carrying standard issue K98 rifles, while several others, whom Dietrich instructed to travel in the trucks towards the back of the convoy, were carrying KP/31 submachine guns.

One particular group of soldiers had caught Ragnar's eye. Earlier, he had seen them huddled outside the ammunitions store long after the other men had started gathering by the convoy vehicles. Dietrich had spent an intense ten minutes talking to them and had seemed especially animated. Ragnar had watched him sketching something out in a notebook.

Now that same party of men was quietly loading something into the back of one of the trucks, which was set apart from the rest of the convoy. Ragnar took a few steps around to the rear of his car to get a better look. There appeared to be three or four similar objects and, from the way the men were carrying them – cautiously, one by one from the ammunitions store – they looked reasonably heavy and were either very fragile or extremely hazardous.

Ragnar moved a little closer. He was desperate to get a clearer view but didn't want to draw attention to himself, so he ducked down, pretending to do up his shoelace. The men had now finished loading and were rapidly covering the back of the truck with a tarpaulin, but Ragnar was just able to catch a glimpse of one of the objects. It was a jerrycan, the standard steel type, built to hold about twenty litres of fuel. Nothing unusual about that, he thought, except that this jerrycan had been hastily modified. Two pieces of wire were tightly taped around it, holding in place a smoke stick grenade.

Ragnar backed slowly towards his car, feeling the hairs standing up on the back of his neck. What had Dietrich got planned? Was this what he had meant by 'shaking the beehive' in Oradour?

Ragnar knew that his boss was ambitious and that he liked to make his mark. How else had he managed to claw his way up through the ranks in the SS so rapidly? Moreover, Ragnar knew that Dietrich was relishing the task of finding the missing Major Klausner before anyone else could. He loved a difficult challenge. He thrived on proving that he was better than all the rest. But what lengths would he really go to? How many times would he feel the need to prove himself to his beloved SS leaders?

Ragnar could see Dietrich now, striding across to the car, gesturing to him to get in. Whatever worries he had, he would have to bury them for the moment. Dietrich was impatient to leave and definitely not in the mood to tolerate any delay.

Dietrich jumped into the seat next to Ragnar and ordered him to speed to the front of the convoy as it pulled out of Saint Junien.

'Follow my directions and don't get too far ahead,' he said quickly, waving a map in his leather-clad hand.

Ragnar nodded, 'We're still heading for Oradour, though, Major, yes?'

'Yes, of course,' Dietrich replied, studying the map. 'But I won't make it easy for the Resistance to track us. If there are any rebels out there, we're going to give them a bit of a run-around. No use in broadcasting our intentions.'

'What exactly are our intentions, Major?' Ragnar asked tentatively, glancing sideways at his boss.

'To take care of one hell of a mess,' said Dietrich

through gritted teeth. 'Turn right here. We'll go round through Saint Victurnien then back onto this road where it crosses the Vienne.'

'But Major General Scholz's orders still stand? We have to establish whether Oradour has any involvement in the kidnapping?'

'Oh, his orders haven't changed,' snorted Dietrich. 'We'll do a thorough search, don't you worry. There'll be nothing left in Oradour *to* search by the time we leave.'

'And if we do find Major Klausner? If the Resistance *have* been keeping him there, do we still take hostages? Still negotiate?' Ragnar had the distinct impression that Dietrich was holding something back.

'Whatever we find,' Dietrich said icily, 'it's far too late to negotiate.' Then, seeing the look of concern on Ragnar's face, he added, 'Don't you worry, my friend. By the end of the day, Major General Scholz will be thanking me. As will the whole German army. I'm about to make our relationship with the Resistance a whole lot easier, and that's what General Müller wants, I know that for certain.'

Ragnar stared straight ahead, his knuckles white on the steering wheel as he negotiated the narrow lanes approaching the River Vienne. He decided that Major Gustav Dietrich was a very dangerous man indeed.

94

As soon as the convoy had crossed the River Vienne, Dietrich ordered Ragnar to turn up a small lane which curved out of sight of the main road and ran down into a grassy field sloping away to the river. The halting convoy parked in the shade of the weeping willow trees lining the river bank and Dietrich called out to the troops to assemble for their briefing papers.

An advance platoon was ordered to leave immediately and to search all the outlying buildings and farms between the Vienne and Oradour. As he explained the route they had to take, Dietrich revealed the first part of his plan.

'Round up anyone you can find. I want them all to be brought into the village. You must not leave any barn, any building, any haystack unturned. No one must be missed. And make it impossible for anyone to go back. If they have slipped through the net, there must be nowhere for them to return to. Nowhere to hide. So burn every building to the ground before you move on.'

A second platoon was instructed to divide up and to seal off all four roads into Oradour. 'We have the advantage of surprise,' said Dietrich. 'And Oradour is defenceless and easy to encircle. There are just four ways in and out: the road to Limoges to the south-east across the River Glane, the road we will use, coming in from Saint Junien, the road to Peyrilhac to the north-east and the road towards Confolens to the north-west. This last road is the main street through the village, Rue Depaul. Once we have sealed off the village, not a soul is to come in or out of that village until I give the order, unless they belong to 3rd Battalion. Is that understood?'

The men nodded, offering a chorus of 'Yes, Major.'

'And I need at least two of you to be ready to stop the trams coming in from Limoges. The station is at the top of the village in Rue Depaul so you will have to intercept them before the road block by the river bridge. Bring the drivers and all the passengers into the village and make sure that no tram leaves before we have completed our mission.'

Three platoons were then given maps of Oradour with orders to cover specific buildings or sections of the streets. The plan, they were told, was simple: they had to evacuate every property in the village and gather the entire population in the village green, known as the fairground. Once the buildings were empty, a full search could be carried out. The search parties were to report to Dietrich, who would be based in the fairground coordinating the mission, and then await their next orders.

Dietrich paused to give his men time to digest what he had said. One of the youngest soldiers, a pimply, blond-haired, nervous-looking man, half raised his hand

and dared to speak. 'Major Dietrich… er, permission to ask a question please, Major?'

Dietrich spun his head round to find the source of the thin, shaky voice. 'Yes? What is it?'

The rest of the troops stared on in stony silence.

'Major, what should we do if anyone refuses to come to the fairground?'

Dietrich shook his head, as if the answer was obvious. 'No one has a choice. It's your job to make sure everyone knows that. I remind you that we have permission from General Müller to take reprisals against anyone who allies themselves with the Resistance. Major General Scholz has asked us to search Oradour for evidence of the kidnap of an SS officer. So treat anyone who refuses to cooperate with suspicion. If they can walk to the fairground, then they must go. No questions asked.'

'But Major…' the young soldier continued despite receiving a hostile glare from Dietrich. 'What if someone is too old or too sick to move? We can't assume that they support the Resistance.'

'Silence!' screamed Dietrich, as a couple of sniggers ran round the gathered troop. 'If they are too old or too sick to walk then just shoot them.'

Dietrich didn't see the look of shock on the young soldier's face as he was already storming off to brief the last group of men.

This final platoon was armed with heavy machine guns. They were given protection duty. They were to provide the troops inside Oradour with any necessary covering fire, explained Dietrich, should there be any attack or trouble outside the road blocks.

As he watched Dietrich moving among his men, clarifying his commands, Ragnar couldn't quell his sense of unease. If this was just a search and rescue mission, why did they need incendiary devices? What had Dietrich really meant when he'd said there would be nothing left in Oradour *to* search?

With their watches synchronised, and satisfied that his men understood their orders, Dietrich gave the advance parties the signal to move out. They had until two o'clock to search the outlying farms and seal off the roads into Oradour before the bulk of the battalion would go in and begin the evacuation of all the buildings. Dietrich would wait there at the Vienne with one final group of men, and would bring up the rear, arriving at the fairground at 2.30.

Dietrich felt a bubble of excitement in his stomach as he watched the first vehicles driving off. It was more than just the pleasure of seeing his plans being put into action, it was the unquestioning respect with which his men carried out his orders. The power, the control, it was always a rush. When he was in charge of his men, he felt in charge of his life.

He strolled confidently over to the river bank and climbed up onto the crumbling wall which formed the old doorway into an abandoned leather works. The noise of the rushing water filled his ears and Dietrich checked his footing as he looked down over the edge into the deep, dark, swirling river. In some places so tranquil and peaceful, here the Vienne was deadly and foreboding.

Dietrich recalled the time when he was seven years old and his mother had persuaded his father to come out of his study and join them for a Sunday picnic on the Dreisam River near Freiburg. It was a hot, sticky summer afternoon and his mother had let Gustav walk down to the river in his bathing suit and sandals. After they had eaten their lunch, Dietrich was allowed to go and play at the water's edge. He had loved playing on the beach, paddling, making dams in the sand and skimming stones across the river. Then he had noticed the deep pool underneath the footbridge. The water looked so cool and clear and he knew how to swim, so he scrambled along the bank and onto the bridge.

He remembered shouting out gleefully to his father, desperate for him to watch him as he jumped. He would be like Johnny Weissmuller, a mini-Tarzan leaping out of the treetops into a jungle pool to bravely fight a crocodile.

The water was deep and his feet only briefly touched the stones on the river bed as he plunged into the pool. He pushed downwards with his hands and kicked, bursting back up out of the water, at the same time spinning round to check that his father hadn't missed his brave leap. But Father wasn't there sitting on the picnic rug next to his mother, clapping and cheering as Gustav had hoped.

Momentarily confused and still treading water in the deep pool, Gustav heard his father before he saw him and he could sense his outrage. He was wading out furiously into the water and when Gustav turned to face him he could see his mouth moving and realised that he was yelling. That was when his father's big hands closed around his arm and he was plucked from the water out onto the shingle bank.

'You stupid, stupid little boy. You could have killed yourself. What on earth did you think you were doing?'

Gustav had tried to make his father understand that he was a good swimmer and it was alright, he knew it was safe, but Father was too angry. He wasn't listening. He didn't even listen to Mother when she said he was over-reacting and asked him not to spoil the day. He simply dragged Gustav back to the picnic rug, threw him down onto the mat and silently began packing up their things. Mother had said that Father was just taking care of his boy, and she had winked at Gustav and wrapped him closely in a towel. But that didn't soothe the huge painful lump that had formed in Gustav's throat nor the stinging of the hot tears as they merged with the cold river water that dripped from his hair. There would be no moment of glory, no laughter, no fun little fantasy shared. The afternoon was over.

That was the last time Father ever came on a family picnic.

A flash of colour caught Dietrich's eye and startled him back to the present. A kingfisher, which had been perched on one of the weeping willows, had darted down into the river, enticed by a silver flash in the water and the promise of food.

It was time to move out. Time for another shot at a moment of glory.

10: THE LONG LUNCH

'COME ON, Bobby,' said Alfred cheerfully, whistling to the little dog who had been loyally waiting for him outside the back door of the Fourniers' cottage. 'I've got to get back to school. Quick! I've only got five minutes.'

Christelle and Sabine had already gone on ahead while Alfred was still lingering over his cheese and bread, less eager to return to the hot and stuffy classroom. And he might have stretched out his lunchtime a little longer had Madame Rousseau not come knocking on the front door. She had dropped by to remind his mother about helping with the church flower arrangements that afternoon, and for some strange reason which Alfred couldn't understand, because he knew his mother didn't particularly like spending time with this rather scary lady, she had been invited in for a cool glass of lemonade. Alfred had no intention of hanging around under Madame Rousseau's critical gaze, so he had

102

stuffed the rest of his bread in his pocket, called out goodbye to his mother and father, and dashed out in the other direction, through the back garden.

Off he and Bobby raced, back down Rue Depaul, past the post office, past the village hall, past the tram station, where day-trippers were still pouring into the village.

They approached the Hotel de la Glane where, to Alfred's surprise, Rachael and Ethan were still sitting at their table, chatting away contentedly in the sunshine. Ethan was tipping the last few drops of a carafe of red wine into his wife's glass.

Bobby sniffed the air, tempted by the scent of the food coming from the hotel kitchens and the little dog would certainly have scurried across to look for some tasty fallen scraps had Alfred not scooped him up into his arms.

'No you don't, little fellow,' Alfred chuckled. 'I haven't got time to chase you around the tables. I'm taking you back to Patric. You will have to stay at the garage until I get out of school.'

But when Alfred arrived outside the double arched wooden doors of Patric Depaul's garage he found them locked and there was no sign of Patric's car outside.

'Oh,' he said out loud. 'I wonder where he is. That's odd, isn't it, Bobby? Patric's usually busy working on a Saturday. Perhaps he's gone out for lunch today.'

Just then, young Philippe the farmer's son walked past, looking very smart in his best suit and carrying a bunch of flowers. He was whistling to himself as he went along, skipping on and off the kerb to dodge all the Saturday shoppers.

'You alright, young Alfie?' he enquired.

'Yes… I mean, no… Well, I have to get back to school quickly and I was hoping to ask Patric to make sure Bobby stayed here, but it's all locked up.'

'Ah, I see. And I don't suppose Monsieur Gravois would approve of an extra pupil – especially one dropping hair and slobber all over the place!'

'No, he definitely wouldn't,' giggled Alfred.

'Well,' said Philippe. 'I have a rather important task to do, but Bobby is welcome to come with me. In fact he might be just the help I need!'

'Oh?' said Alfred, raising his eyebrows quizzically.

'You see…' Philippe lent his head close to Alfred and dropped his voice to a whisper, 'I am off to ask Nadia to marry me.'

Philippe and Nadia, the hotel chef's daughter, had been courting for the past year.

'Wow,' said Alfred, 'that's brilliant! But how can Bobby help?'

'Nadia is a soft touch for animals. She loves coming to see the lambs and the calves on the farm. So, if Bobby comes with me and wags his tail at the right moment...'

'That sounds like a fine idea,' said Alfred, glad to have found someone to look after his little friend. 'Do you hear that, Bobby? You have to tell Nadia to say "yes".' And with one quick stroke of the dog's head, he was gone, racing off down the street in the direction of his school.

PART 4

SATURDAY 10 JUNE, 1944 (EARLY AFTERNOON)

11: THE TROOPS ARRIVE

BY TWO o'clock, the terrace at the Hotel de la Glane was finally beginning to empty, and the diners, re-energised and refreshed, began to drift away to spend the afternoon visiting friends, lazing by the river or browsing the shops and street stalls.

Patric Depaul drove his Peugeot 202 over the bridge across the river Glane and slowed down as he entered his home village. He had bought the parts he needed for his father's car and had made the nineteen-kilometre drive back from Limoges in good time. Now he was looking forward to getting back to the garage so he could complete the job and finish up early for the day.

If he had a spare hour or two before dinner, he could even squeeze in a spot of fishing. He would take Bobby with him. That daft little dog loved sniffing about on the river bank while Patric fished, but he didn't like the water. He never went in, no matter how hot it was. Funny, that.

Patric pulled up outside his garage and switched off the ignition. As always, he paused to listen to the engine as it rumbled to a stop. *Yep*, he thought, *she sounds happy enough*. Then his mechanically-trained ears picked up the sound of several much heavier vehicles, also approaching from the direction of Limoges.

Patric got out of his car and shielded his eyes with his hand, squinting in the bright sunlight as he looked up the street to see what was causing the commotion. This didn't sound like ordinary village traffic. A deep engine rumble was accompanied by a dreadful metallic, clanking sound.

What Patric saw next did not immediately alarm him, although it was an unusual sight for Oradour — two armoured vehicles followed by a convoy of smaller army trucks laden with German soldiers. Patric's first thought was that they were just passing through, but then the convoy stopped opposite the hotel, across the entrance to the fairground, and to his astonishment, a flood of German soldiers, dressed in green and yellow camouflage jackets, poured out into the street. The troops formed a circle around the convoy and slowly started spreading outwards in all directions.

Losing all thought of fixing his father's car, Patric ran around the street corner back towards the church. Were there any more soldiers coming?

As he passed the barber's shop, he heard a shout. 'Patric, quick, come over here!'

It was Jean Neville, scissors and comb in hand, standing in his doorway. 'Did you see that convoy? Where did it go?'

Patric explained what he had just witnessed.

'One of my customers has just arrived from Confolens for a haircut. He said there's another group of soldiers up by the Fourniers' cottage at the far end of village. They closed the road just after he came through. What the devil's going on?'

'I have no idea,' said Patric, 'but I'll go back down to the Glane, to see if they've closed that road, too.'

Patric jogged down the road then ascended the steep path in front of the church. As the church was set up above street level, he could stand on the boundary wall and get a clear view down the hill back towards the bridge. Sure enough, he could see more Germans, dragging a barricade across the road on the far side of the river.

He didn't like the look of this one bit.

Patric wondered what was happening on the road to the north east, beyond Alfred's school, and on the road south-west towards Saint Junien. It didn't take a betting man to predict that those roads were probably being closed too, and this was bound to create unease. The people of Oradour weren't used to seeing Germans at all, let alone having them seal off their village.

Patric decided to head back into the village centre. He would see if his father was at home. As Mayor, he ought to know what was going on. Perhaps he could speak to the Germans and find out what they wanted.

As he followed the road back round past his garage, Patric saw Sylvie Fournier, Alfred's mother, hurrying down the street towards him.

'Sylvie, are you all right?' he asked, catching her arm. She looked awfully worried.

'I don't know,' Sylvie answered, seemingly unsure whether or not to carry on her way. 'I have to get to the church to help Audrey... but did you see those Germans? I've just spoken to Pierre Petit – he was coming out of the wine store when the trucks arrived – and he says there's nothing to worry about, but I'm not sure I agree.'

'I am sure Pierre's right,' said Patric, trying not to show his own fears. He could see that Sylvie was getting more and more agitated by the second. 'We've never had any trouble with Germans here in Oradour.'

'Maybe not, but I wouldn't trust them as far as I could throw them, and I've left little Paulette and Louis with Leon. They're in the fairground getting tobacco. Alfred and the two girls are down at the school… and here I am, worrying about upsetting Audrey over some stupid flower arrangements! We have a family pact, you see, something we agreed to do if we ever saw any Germans in Oradour.'

'Look, Sylvie, I know what you've gone through. But this is different. This is Oradour. You are safe here. I'm sure you don't need to worry, but if you like I'll pop back into the church and explain to Audrey that you're going to be delayed. Then you can go and check on your family. Audrey will just have to understand.'

Tears came to Sylvie's eyes and she squeezed Patric's hand. 'Thank you, Patric. You're a good friend. Tell her I'll come back as soon as I can. But I have to put my family first.'

And with that, Sylvie ran off up the street to find her husband and her two youngest children, desperately trying to convince herself that history was not about to be repeated.

12: NO TURNING BACK

DIETRICH HARDLY uttered a word to Ragnar as their car raced through the lanes towards Oradour. With the rest of the battalion already in place in the village, Dietrich was no longer concerned about possible Resistance attacks so he changed his order to take a circuitous route to a demand to get to Oradour as fast as possible.

Ragnar knew that the Major would not be interested in making conversation. He was completely absorbed in his own thoughts, his mouth moving silently as if he were running through in his head the orders he had given to his men. Beads of sweat stood out on his forehead and his steel-blue eyes glinted with anticipation.

They approached the road block before the river bridge at exactly twenty-five minutes past two, and it was only then that Ragnar slowed down the car, enabling Dietrich to salute his men as they dragged the temporary barrier aside to let them through.

They drove, slowly now, up past the church which perched on the slope above them on their left. They began to pass shops and stores – a café, a barber's, a cobbler's and a bakery – all full of customers, then a neat row of well-kept houses, their freshly-painted shutters closed to keep the rooms inside cool. Ragnar noticed Dietrich suddenly shifting in his seat.

'It's busier than I expected.' These were the first words he had spoken since they had left the Vienne.

Ragnar dared a reply. 'I believe it's often busy in Oradour on a Saturday. All the locals come here for their tobacco rations, but I think there is something going on in the school today, too. I heard one of the soldiers talking. A health inspection or something.' He took his eyes off the road and turned to meet Dietrich's gaze directly. 'So that means there will be a lot more children here than normal, Major.'

If this information made any difference to Dietrich, he did not show it.

'Turn right here,' was all he said, ignoring the look of concern on Ragnar's face and glancing down instead at his map. They had come to a junction. A handwritten sign was painted on the wall: '*Cimetière*'.

'Yes, here. This is the road up to the cemetery. It should bring us to the back entrance into the village green. They call it the fairground.'

112

Dietrich was right. As they turned into the fairground, they could see that the troops had already gathered a small crowd of civilians and were directing them to go and stand in the centre of the grassy, open space, where a row of soldiers carrying rifles watched over them.

Ragnar parked the car next to a well. This was his last chance. He had to find out what Dietrich really wanted to achieve in Oradour, why he had brought those incendiary devices, so many men. And he knew he was one of the few people who could even dare to ask the Major a question like this.

'Major, wait,' he said quickly, as Dietrich opened the passenger door and started to get out of the car. 'Forgive me, but…' He paused, even then unsure whether or not to risk his boss's wrath.

'Spit it out, man. What is it?' Dietrich ducked his head back inside the car, his face tense, one hand gripping the top rim of the door.

'Major, do you intend to burn something down in this village?'

Dietrich froze. Ragnar noticed a tiny twitch in the corner of his left eye. Then he said coolly, 'You can take this car back to Saint Junien. I won't be needing you any more. I'll travel back with my men.'

A rush of warm summer air hit Ragnar in the face as the car door slammed shut, and he closed his eyes for a

113

moment and exhaled. When he opened them again, he looked about him, taking in the scene in the fairground – the huddle of curious villagers waiting patiently in the middle of the grass, the old woman dressed all in black sitting in the shade of a tree, the man arguing with his wife about losing his place in the tobacco queue, while his two little children sat on the kerbside, the young man in mechanic's overalls banging on the door of the large house on the far side of the field… and the long, slender back of Major Gustav Dietrich as he marched off, eager to liaise with his troops. Then Ragnar turned the key in the ignition and slowly drove away, leaving the idyllic little village of Oradour behind him.

13: THE SUMMONS

AS SOON as Major Gustav Dietrich arrived in the fairground, things began to move more rapidly. His first action was to summon the Mayor of Oradour, Henri Depaul.

The Mayor, he was told, lived just across the fairground and was on his way. His son, Patric, had already been to alert him to the Germans' arrival.

Despite the heat of the June afternoon, the burly authoritative figure who marched across the grass towards Dietrich was dressed in a smart dark suit, complete with a crisply-pressed jacket and tie. The glare of the bright afternoon sun on his white hair gave his face an almost ethereal glow and, as he grew closer, Dietrich could see a firm, square jawline and a mouth framed by a neatly trimmed handlebar moustache. Dietrich was amused by the fact that, in his left hand, the Mayor carried a leather briefcase, as if he was entering a routine business meeting.

Walking closely at his side was a younger man wearing a mechanic's overall. Despite the differences in their attire, there was enough of a similarity between the two for Dietrich to deduce that they were father and son.

The Mayor did not look happy. He was outraged at this sudden intrusion into his otherwise peaceful village, and he was muttering something under his breath to his son as he approached.

The two men came face to face and the Mayor didn't wait to be addressed.

'I'm Henri Depaul. I'm the Mayor of this village. Would you mind telling me what's going on?'

Dietrich's interpreter stepped forward and gestured to Henri as he translated the Mayor's words into German.

'I am sure you'd like to know,' Dietrich answered, smiling patronisingly at the Mayor. 'I am Major Gustav Dietrich and I have orders to carry out a thorough identity check here in your fine little village. We need to round up every last person here – not just residents of Oradour, we want to see all visitors, too.'

Henri forced a smile. He didn't like this cocky young officer with his SS cap, complete with silver skull-and-crossbones, tilted arrogantly to one side. But he could see from the Iron Cross on his breast pocket, and the way his men kowtowed around him, that he was not someone it would be wise to antagonise.

'Of course. We will help in any way we can. But, Major, can I ask what it is that has brought you here? Why Oradour?'

'That's of no concern to you at this stage,' Dietrich replied through the interpreter. 'Just help us to get everyone down here to the fairground, and quickly. Tell them that all we want to do is check papers. You have fifteen minutes.'

Henri turned to Patric and asked him to fetch the town crier and set him to work immediately.

'Wait!' shouted Dietrich, pushing one of his SS officers towards Patric. 'Take this officer with you. He can speak fluent French. He's to accompany the town crier at all times. Now go. *Schnell! Vite!*'

As they stood on the other side of the fairground, Sylvie and Leon Fournier watched this exchange anxiously, holding little Paulette and Louis tightly by the hand.

'Did you hear that, Sylvie?' Leon whispered. 'It's going to be alright. They only want to check that everyone has their identity papers. We should be fine. All our papers are in order, I'll just run back and get them. It won't take me long. You stay here with the children. Just do whatever they ask.'

'But Leon, this isn't what we agreed,' Sylvie declared, fear making her voice shake. 'If Alfie and the girls see the Germans here they'll go straight to the cemetery. We should do the same. We should stay together.'

'What's wrong, Maman?' It was Louis, feeling his mother's hand trembling in his.

Leon glared at his wife. 'Come on, Sylvie. You have to stay calm. You're frightening the children. I'll be ten minutes at the most, I promise.'

Sylvie relented, her thoughts suddenly turning to their friends, Ethan and Rachael. She let go of Louis' hand and grasped her husband's arm. Looking quickly around her to check that she was well out of anyone's earshot, she said in a low voice, 'You've got to warn Rachael and Ethan. If the Germans suspect that they're Jewish, they'll be in real trouble. Maybe they should try and get out of Oradour? If they risk coming here to the fairground...'

Leon nodded. 'Yes, good idea. I'd better hurry.'

He gave his wife a hug, smiled at the children and then ran off up the street in the direction of home, passing the town crier, now banging his drum in a solemn but steady rhythm, broadcasting his message around the streets.

Following Dietrich's orders, the soldiers of the 3rd Battalion swept their way through Oradour, home by home, shop by shop, street by street, hammering on doors, breaking into locked rooms, checking all the alleyways and searching back yards.

Gradually, the fairground began to fill with the people they rounded up. Despite the suddenness of the Germans' arrival, everyone remained relatively calm, accepting the reassurance being offered that this was simply an identity check.

Sylvie gathered the children close to her skirt and went to sit in the shade of the tree. She was determined to stay out of the way and out of any trouble. She saw some of her friends and neighbours coming into the fairground. One of the first was Jean Neville, still wearing his white barber's shirt and leading a small band of disgruntled clients. His customer from Confolens, a short, dumpy man with a thin black moustache, was cursing and gesticulating rudely. Jean had been half way through his haircut when the German soldier had come into the shop to order them outside and he was embarrassed to be seen with one side of his hair shorter than the other. Another client was wiping the shaving foam from his face with his sleeve as he walked.

Then Sylvie saw Leon's boss, Benoit, leading his wife Blanche across the road, his floury arm placed protectively around her shoulder. He sat Blanche down next to Sylvie then went over to one of the soldiers standing guard.

'How long is this going to take?' he asked. 'I still have bread in the ovens and it's going to spoil if I don't get back quickly. No one likes burned bread.'

But the soldier either didn't understand French or didn't know the answer to the question, as he just pushed Benoit away with the end of his rifle and flicked his head to one side, to direct him to go and sit down.

'How very rude. That's most unnecessary,' commented Blanche disapprovingly. Then she nudged Sylvie and pointed up towards the village well. 'Oh my goodness, look at that! The poor dear.'

Madame Roux, the headmistress of the Oradour School for Girls was shuffling sheepishly into the fairground wearing a quilted dressing gown over a bright pink nightdress. Madame Roux had been at home nursing a nasty case of flu and a raging temperature, yet even so she had been dragged out to join her fellow villagers. Normally such a proud lady, she was cringing with the shame of being seen out in her bed clothes and looking so dishevelled. As she stood blowing her nose in the middle of the growing crowd, Sylvie could see her swaying. She looked quite dizzy and very sorry for herself.

Sylvie also noticed that, as they arrived in the fairground, all the men were being asked to surrender any weapons. Most of them reluctantly complied, not wanting to stir up any trouble, but for Philippe, buoyant and full of confidence after having his proposal of marriage to his sweetheart accepted just a few moments before, this was a step too far. With his new fiancée at his side he was determined not to be pushed around.

'Look, I'm a farmer. This is for hunting,' he argued, when the SS officer demanded that he hand over his shotgun. 'It's my right to carry it. Since when was it a crime to put food on the table?'

'Hand it over now, or I'll shoot you *and* your girlfriend,' the soldier yelled, aiming his rifle in Philippe's face.

Sylvie pulled Paulette and Louis to her breast so that they couldn't watch.

'Alright, alright,' Philippe said, immediately dropping his gun to the floor and kicking it across to the German. 'I'm sorry.'

He turned away, red-faced, and took Nadia's hand with a sheepish smile. Nadia was clearly not impressed and shook her head at him crossly, muttering in his ear.

Sylvie could hear Philippe offering more apologies as the couple pulled back into the crowd. *Foolish boy*, she thought to herself. *He's got no idea.*

As the minutes passed, the noise level in the fairground started to rise. The tapping of the children's clogs on the cobbles, the heavy thud of the soldiers' boots, the distant shouting from the German search parties, the anxious chatter of the villagers as they debated what would happen next, all a far contrast to the silence which rapidly descended on the now empty streets.

The grassy area in front of Sylvie was filling up – day trippers, shopkeepers, farmers, fishermen, mothers cuddling young babies, older sisters and brothers helping to push prams – and Sylvie had to keep standing up and straining her neck to see over the crowd, to see if she could spot Leon returning with their papers. Every so often, she glanced in the other direction, towards the road out to Peyrilhac and the refugee school. Some of the pupils who had been allowed to finish at lunchtime were milling around in the fairground, hanging off their parents' arms or kicking around in the dust, looking irritable and bored. Sylvie prayed that Christelle, Sabine and Alfie were still safe in the classroom.

'So much for getting the flower arrangements done!'

Sylvie jumped up as Madame Rousseau's imposing shadow fell across her lap.

'Oh, Audrey, I'm so sorry. I was on my way to the church when all this started. I had to come and find the children, I hope you understand.'

'Of course I do, dear,' said Audrey, patting her arm. 'You must have been quite scared. I know this must bring back some bad memories. And don't worry, Patric told me where you were.'

There it was again, that gentle thoughtfulness that lay underneath the prickly outer layer, the side that Audrey had revealed when the Fourniers had first arrived in Oradour. Sylvie felt a sudden rush of warmth for her neighbour and more than a little guilt about her reluctance to spend time with her.

'He's a good man, Patric Depaul,' Audrey added. 'I know he was anxious to get up here quickly, to warn his father, but he still took the time to walk with me. I think he could tell I was worried. They've been bursting into people's houses you know, dragging them out. Old Armand the butcher's father, came out half-dressed, still in his vest. Poor old soul. I really don't know why they have to rush everyone so much.'

Sylvie was only half listening to Audrey. Her fears multiplying, she was still searching the growing mass of people, looking for Leon. Then, to her relief, she saw him, pushing his way through the crowd towards her and the children, their identity documents clutched in his hand.

'Did you get everything?' Sylvie asked, raising her eyebrows to hint at what she was really enquiring about.

'Yes, I did. All safe.' Leon smiled at Audrey politely and then took Sylvie to one side. 'They're hiding,' he whispered. 'In a cubby hole under the stairs. Rachael was distraught but I think I managed to calm her down when I told her they were just checking identity papers. So as long as they stay well out of sight for a while, they should be fine.'

'Good,' said Sylvie, although she was not completely reassured.

'I think quite a few others are hiding too,' Leon added quietly. 'I met Patric by the hotel and he told me that Monsieur Lefevre didn't want to wait to find out what the Germans wanted. He snuck out the back of his smithy as soon as he saw them coming over the bridge. He's run off over the fields towards Peyrilhac. The family from the mill have gone with him, but they are Jewish, so I can't blame them.'

'Then we should go too, Leon,' pleaded Sylvie. 'That's what we always agreed. We should go to the cemetery. If anything happens, at least Alfred and the girls will know where to look for us.'

'Not yet,' whispered Leon. 'The Germans are searching everywhere. Another tram came into town just now and the driver said he'd seen troops searching all the farms around here. He saw them probing haystacks with bayonets. So they're bound to check the cemetery. If they found us there they'd think we were resisting or had something to hide. No. Our papers are in order and we should wait this out.'

Sylvie nodded and sat down again next to Louis and Paulette, who were busy digging holes in the dirt with a stick. She knew that Leon was making sense and she knew that he would do anything to keep the family safe. He had brought them all the way across France, after all, here to Oradour. He'd given them a fresh start, new hope. She had to trust him.

But there was one thing that was still bothering her. If this was really just an identity check, why had no one, not a soul so far as she could see, been asked to show their papers?

14: THE NEGOTIATION

LESS THAN an hour after the first German convoy arrived in Oradour, more than six hundred people made their way into the fairground: the villagers, all the day visitors, and the hundred and fifty or more folk who had been brought in by German trucks from neighbouring villages and surrounding farms.

All the time, Major Gustav Dietrich was strutting about in the centre of the crowd like a cockerel in a yard. It was now time for him to crow. He climbed up onto the bonnet of one of the battalion's jeeps and announced that he wanted to speak to the Mayor again.

Henri Depaul had been busy trying to reassure the people of his village, moving among them on the field and doing his best to keep everyone calm. Now he heard his name being called and, supposing the Major wanted him to help organise the identity paper inspections, wasted no time in heading across to hear what Dietrich had to say.

As soon as Dietrich spied the Mayor approaching, he raised his hand in the air and the crowd fell silent.

'Now we have you all gathered here, we can get down to business.'

As he paused to allow his interpreter to translate, Dietrich scanned all the faces looking expectantly up at him. He smiled, like a host getting ready to welcome his party guests. But as he spoke his next words, his face fell deadly serious and his voice took on a steely edge.

'A German officer, a major in the SS, has been taken hostage. We are here to give you people the chance to tell us where he is.'

Dietrich stopped, observing carefully the shockwave which ran through the crowd. Some people gasped, some looked about them in confusion, others stood completely still, too stunned to move. There was a sudden hum of whispering and murmuring. Sylvie and Leon reached for one another's hands.

Dietrich continued. 'If anyone is involved in this terrible crime, or has any information at all to share, then they are advised to step forward now. I am giving you all one minute.'

Dietrich looked at his watch, then jumped down confidently from the jeep. While the seconds ticked away he spoke intently into the ear of one of his platoon leaders, who immediately marched off towards the platoons which had completed their initial search of the village and were awaiting their next orders.

Fifty-eight seconds, fifty-nine, sixty, and nothing.

Dietrich leapt back up onto his makeshift podium and opened his mouth to address the crowd again, but before he uttered a word he was interrupted by Henri Depaul. This time it was the Mayor who raised his hand to ask for silence, before he called out, 'Wait. Please, Major. I request permission to speak on behalf of my people.'

Dietrich appeared irritated and for a moment Henri thought that he was about to refuse his request, but then the German spread his hands, turning his palms upwards to indicate that the Mayor was allowed to speak.

'It doesn't matter how many minutes you give us, Major, no one here will have anything to tell you. Because Oradour is innocent. We have no connection with the hostage-taking. No links to the Resistance. We hide nothing.'

Dietrich's eyes narrowed.

'I see. And you think that I will believe you? That in the midst of all the Resistance attacks and in spite of reports to the contrary, your village has no involvement? No secret weapons stores? No Resistance sympathisers?

No knowledge of the whereabouts of the hostage?'

The Mayor shook his head, dismayed by the German's change of tone. 'I give you my word.'

Dietrich shook his head and gave a mocking laugh. 'Oh, you will give me more than that, Monsieur le Maire. You will give me thirty hostages. Thirty reasons for the Resistance to come forward. Thirty bits of bait to entice those cowardly little mice out of their holes.'

Henri looked horrified and swallowed hard. 'Thirty?'

'Yes,' said Dietrich, jumping down again from the jeep to speak right into the face of the panic-stricken Mayor. 'Thirty of your finest citizens, and you can choose every last one of them.'

Cries of anguish went up from the crowd, pitying the poor Mayor. Normally so self-controlled, he was now completely perplexed, standing there looking wildly about him. How could he possibly make such an appalling choice?

The first to Henri's side was Patric, who took his father's elbow and spoke urgently in his ear. Henri nodded his head, said a few words in return, then put his arms around his son and hugged him tightly. He composed himself, then turned back to face Dietrich. He cleared his throat, and made his offer.

'You ask the impossible of me. I will not put thirty of my citizens in danger. But I will offer myself and my four sons as your hostages. Patric here is a well-respected local businessman. My eldest son Bertrand is a doctor and a man of great status in the community. Eriq is my secretary and my other son, Oliver, is the village grocer. Five of us. All good men. We would provide you with all the bargaining power you would need.'

Dietrich laughed. He was like a lion toying with a mouse. 'Your selflessness and courage is admirable, sir. But I will not allow your family to make martyrs of yourselves.'

'And I cannot play games with people's lives,' said Henri, his desperation turning to frustration. 'I will not choose who stays and who goes.'

'Then the negotiation is over!' Dietrich shouted, instantly turning his back on the Mayor to storm off and speak with his men. The stunned crowd interpreted Dietrich's reaction as pure anger but, had they been able to see his face, they would have witnessed the smug, self-satisfied smile that curled on his lips.

For Dietrich, everything was going exactly according to plan.

Without hesitation, Dietrich summoned his platoon leaders. They were to meet him in the village hall in five minutes. They were about to receive a new brief.

The moment Dietrich departed, the noise level in the fairground rose to fever pitch as endless questions buzzed in the air. What did this mean? What was going to happen next? Why did the Germans think Oradour was involved in the hostage taking? Didn't they realise that they had made a terrible mistake?

For Sylvie and Leon, the failed negotiation between the German commander and their Mayor was a crucial turning point. When they saw Dietrich storming off, they looked at one another and instantly knew they were thinking the same thing. It was time to get out, time to keep to their pact and make their way, no matter how long it took them, to the woods behind the cemetery.

'Come on, children,' Leon whispered to Louis and Paulette. 'We're going to play a little game. It's a bit like hide and seek. We're going to try to find Alfred, Christelle and Sabine. But you must be really quiet and not tell anyone where we're going. It's a secret game. No one must suspect that we are playing it. Yes?'

Louis and Paulette nodded in agreement, their wide, innocent eyes filled with excitement.

Taking their children's hands, Leon and Sylvie started to edge their way cautiously through the crowd towards the well.

'If anyone asks, just say we're trying to get a better view of what's going on,' Leon said softly into Sylvie's ear. 'Just walk slowly. We mustn't run until we get out of sight round the corner into Rue de la Cimetière. We mustn't draw attention to ourselves.'

Sylvie smiled nervously at her husband. She could sense that under his cool exterior he was really as scared as she was and she thought how much she loved this man, who wanted so much to take care of his family and keep them safe.

The meeting between Dietrich and his platoon leaders in the village hall lasted only ten minutes but by the end of it, no one was in any doubt what Dietrich's real plan was.

'Our orders were to ask for hostages, and we have,' said Dietrich, pacing back and forth. 'They had their chance to pick their victims, but they have refused. Now we can punish them all.'

'But what about the search, sir?' one officer asked, not alone in his confusion.

'There's nothing to find,' spat Dietrich. 'Klausner is already dead!'

Seeing the soldiers' confusion, he explained, 'My informants in St Junien confirmed it. He was burned alive – a hero of Germany, brutally murdered! His body was found in an abandoned barn outside Limoges.'

The men exchanged silent glances.

Dietrich continued. 'This is our opportunity to get a grip on the Resistance once and for all. Oradour will be Major Klausner's revenge. A lesson to the Resistance all over France. A masterpiece!' Dietrich stared into each of his men's eyes as he walked among them. 'Are you with me, or not?'

With no one daring to refuse, Dietrich delivered his new orders swiftly and refused to take any questions. If any of their men wavered, he said, the platoon leaders were to remind them what the Resistance were capable of. They were to think about Major Klausner and what had nearly happened to Storm Leader Goth. This was their chance to be heroes. To defend their fellow SS, to show their dedication to their country. There were to be no prisoners, no exceptions... and there was to be no mercy.

No one seemed to notice Leon and Sylvie leading their children surreptitiously to the back of the crowd, and they reached the well with relative ease. From there, it was just a few more metres to the end of the fairground and the turning into Rue de la Cimetière, but two half-covered trucks parked across the road obscured their view. There was no way of knowing if the Germans were guarding the route they needed to take.

'Stay here,' said Leon. 'I'll sneak in between the trucks and take a look. If it's clear, I'll signal you and the children to follow, yes?'

Sylvie nodded her agreement and waited, putting her finger to her lips to remind the children to stay quiet.

Leon darted out from the back of the crowd and shot between the two vehicles. From where she stood, Sylvie could see only his feet, clad in leather boots. The boots had come to a stop. Leon must be able to see round the corner now. She prayed that the way was clear.

Sylvie raised her eyes from the ground expecting to see Leon reappearing in the gap, ready to give her the yes or no signal, but when he did re-emerge it was with his two hands in the air, a look of total despair on his face. Walking behind him, pressing a rifle into his back, was a young SS officer.

Sylvie instinctively stepped forwards, ready to help her husband. She would explain that it was her fault. She'd pretend that she had asked him to go and look for one of their children who had gone missing. The soldier had to understand.

But the soldier just pushed her roughly away.

'*Nein,*' he said. '*Frauen und Kinder müssen nach rechts zu gehen.*'

'I don't understand,' cried Sylvie. 'Leon, what's he saying?'

Leon shook his head in bewilderment as he was led off, away from Sylvie and the children, to join a crowd of men gathering in front of the Mayor's house.

'They've started to separate the men from the women and children,' interjected a young woman nearby, cradling a small baby in her arms. 'We have to go and stand on this side of the green, to the right, in front of the café and the hardware store. The men have to go to the left. Come on, come with us.'

Sylvie could feel tears brimming in her eyes. As she followed the young mother, keeping Louis and Paulette closely in tow, she looked back over her shoulder to try to catch sight of Leon, but he had already disappeared into the crowd.

'Where are they taking Papa?' Louis wailed. 'What about our game?'

'Sshh,' said Sylvie, trying her best to put on a brave face. 'The soldiers just want to talk to him. We'll carry on playing later.'

Inside, Sylvie was in turmoil. They had waited too long. They should never have stayed in the fairground. They had broken their pact.

She began to pray that Alfred, Christelle and Sabine would not make the same mistake.

It was then that Sylvie heard the first terrifying sounds of machine gun fire.

135

15: ALFRED'S CHOICE

BY 2.45, all of the children in Alfred's class had seen Doctor Depaul and were looking forward to being dismissed for the rest of the afternoon. The doctor had left about half an hour earlier, so the children knew they would be going home soon.

Although they were disappointed about having to come back into school after lunch, the afternoon had started on a cheerful note. Monsieur Gravois had invited them all to sing 'Happy Birthday' to Didier, who was ten years old that day, and Didier had proudly shared out some tiny home-made jam tarts, sent in by his mother.

Didier was a friend of Sabine's and had been to the Fournier house many times. Alfred didn't like it when Didier came round because that usually meant he walked home with them from school. All the way, Didier would try to make Sabine laugh with his silly jokes and usually Alfred was the butt of them. He called him Ginger Top and Carrot Boy and, because he was so much taller than Alfred, kept rubbing his knuckles on the top of his head.

Now, as the afternoon drew on, Alfred was getting increasingly restless and was keeping himself entertained by flicking screwed up pieces of paper, dipped into the little white porcelain pot in his desk and soaked in blue ink, at the back of Didier's head with a ruler. So far he had scored three direct hits and Monsieur Gravois still hadn't noticed.

In fact, thinking about it, Monsieur Gravois was decidedly distracted. A short while before, the children had heard some heavy footsteps marching past the school in the direction of the village centre. They were desperate to run to the windows to see who it was but Monsieur Gravois had told them firmly to stay in their seats. He had gone to the school door and looked out, but he must have seen nothing of interest because he came straight back in and shut the door quickly behind him, saying it was nothing, and that the children should get out their reading books.

Alfred stopped firing pellets and peered closely at Monsieur Gravois, who was now pacing up and down in front of his chalkboard, holding a book but definitely not reading it. He was white-faced and was chewing his bottom lip. Something was wrong. What was Monsieur

Gravois waiting for? Doctor Depaul had been gone for ages. Why hadn't he let them go home yet? Was it something to do with the footsteps they had heard outside? What had he really seen out of the window?

Then Alfred nearly jumped out of his seat.

Gunshots. Not far away.

The children all stopped reading and looked about them in bewilderment. Monsieur Gravois dashed over to the window.

The gunfire was followed by shouts. Men's voices. German voices.

Alfred turned round to look at his sisters sitting in the back row with the other older students. Christelle was staring intently at Monsieur Gravois, waiting to see what he would do next. Sabine was sitting bolt upright staring back at her brother, gripping the edge of her desk, her knuckles pale.

More gunfire. Louder now.

'Get down!' screamed Monsieur Gravois. 'Lie face down on the floor!'

The children scrambled for the floor, sending pencils, rulers and exercise books flying. Several of the children were whimpering in fear. The girl next to Alfred began to cry. Another sobbed, 'I want my mother.'

Alfred began to crawl under the desks across the chalk-dusty floor towards his sisters, who were lying side by side. Christelle had her arm laid protectively over her younger sister's back.

'We've got to get out,' he said softly when he reached them.

'Quiet!' said Monsieur Gravois, hearing him. 'Lie still.'

Alfred looked imploringly at Christelle, but she just shook her head quickly.

Maybe Christelle is right, thought Alfred. *We should wait to see what happens next. The Germans might just pass by.*

But they didn't.

The door burst open and in strode a dark-haired German soldier carrying a sub-machine gun.

'Out!' he shouted. 'All of you. Out!'

Monsieur Gravois got rapidly to his feet. More children started to cry.

'Everyone stay calm. It will be all right. Just do as he says. Line up along the wall then follow me.' Monsieur Gravois turned to the soldier and spoke in German. 'They're only children. Where do we have to go?'

'To the fairground. Tell them that their parents are all there. You lead. I will stay at the back. Tell them no one must try to escape.'

At the back of the line, Alfred was tugging at Christelle's sleeve and gesturing with his head towards the door in the corner of the classroom which led to the cloakroom.

'Stop it, Alfred,' Christelle whispered. 'You heard what Monsieur Gravois said. Our parents are all in the fairground.'

'But we all agreed,' argued Alfred. 'It's happening. The Germans have come. We have to go to the woods behind the cemetery. Now, while he's not looking, let's hide in the cloakroom 'til he's gone.'

Christelle looked unmoved.

'Sabine, please,' Alfred pleaded, looking at the younger of his two sisters. 'They're Germans. We know what they're like. They'll try to hurt us.'

Sabine looked from Alfred to Christelle, then back at Alfred. Tears were streaming down her face. 'No,' she said. 'I want to go and find Mother and Father, at the fairground.'

Alfred started to back up into the corner of the classroom, all the time keeping his eyes firmly fixed on the German soldier who was waving his gun at the children at the front of the line to encourage them to start filing out.

'I'm going to try to escape.'

Christelle opened her mouth to object, but Alfred had already ducked out through the doorway and was gone.

The two girls resisted the temptation to look back as they were herded out of the school building, not wanting to raise any suspicion about their brother. They held tightly onto one another's hands, and shuffled along at the back of the line, keeping their heads down.

To get to the fairground they had to walk all the way back up the Peyrilhac road, and then turn right up the hill as they approached the church.

As they reached the end of the road by the blacksmith's, they passed a group of young tourists who had just ridden into town on their bicycles. Christelle heard them desperately trying to explain to the German officer who was shepherding them that they had just come into Oradour for a picnic by the river. They often did it, they kept repeating, it was such a beautiful spot. Could they not just go back down to the bridge? They would find another place to stop.

The SS officer, impatient and tired of listening, suddenly stopped in his tracks and ordered the group to lean their bicycles against the wall. Christelle watched as he marched them at gunpoint into the forge.

It wasn't until the line of schoolchildren had turned off into Rue de la Cimetière that Christelle heard the gunfire from the forge. She closed her eyes and fought back the wave of nausea that rose up in her throat. Alfred had been right. They should have tried to escape. She was the eldest. She should have known better, should have had more courage.

'Do whatever they say, Sabine,' she muttered, squeezing her sister's hand. 'Just don't argue with them, alright?'

Every house and store they passed seemed to be swarming with SS men.

'What are they looking for?' whispered Sabine.

Christelle shook her head in bewilderment.

An old man, hardly able to walk, was being dragged out of his house, his small frail body looking so fragile in the clutches of the powerful young soldier who now shoved him down onto the ground.

'Don't look,' cried Christelle, spinning her sister to face the other way as she saw the rifle being pushed into the old man's back and heard the crack as it fired.

The children were now screaming and Monsieur Gravois, panicking, began to run with them towards the fairground, trying all the while to keep the smallest huddled as close to him as possible. It was too late now to try to quieten their fears, as the gunfire continued to rattle around them and the streets began to fill with the sound of panicked voices.

Once in the cloakroom, Alfred paused for a second, trying to decide his next move. If he went out of the side door, he could escape through the playground and run off in the opposite direction to the way his classmates had gone. But that would mean staying on the road where there was every chance that there would be more soldiers. It also took him towards the river and away from the cemetery.

No. He had to stick to the plan, even if Sabine and Christelle had chosen not to. He had let his mother down too many times lately. He recalled the look on her face the night before as she had served him that plate of dried-up fish stew. This time he was going to do as he was told.

Above his head, offering a view out over the hill at the back of the school, was a small window. It was big enough for him to climb through, and it was open. Alfred put one foot up on the bench under which the pupils all stored their bags and their plimsolls ready for sports lessons, took hold of a coat peg with his left hand, and sprang upwards, grasping the window ledge with his right hand before heaving himself up until he was balanced in mid air, half in and half out. He looked out and could have cried with relief to see the garden and the cornfield beyond free of soldiers. He had a chance.

Swivelling his body round to the side, and hanging on tight, Alfred swung his left leg up. As he lifted his foot over the window sill his clog caught on the latch and he wobbled dangerously. Steadying himself, he tugged with his foot. He was free, but he felt his clog come loose and his breath caught in his throat as it fell back inside. Alfred froze as he waited for it to hit the tiled cloakroom floor, but the noise of the last few children filing out of the classroom disguised the sound. He could still escape.

He swung both legs out of the open window until he was facing back into the cloakroom, then gradually lowered himself down, feet first, as far as he could before letting his body drop to the floor onto the soft grass. Thankful that the ground was dry, Alfred kicked off his remaining clog and sprinted across the grass and scrambled over the wall at the end of the school garden.

He looked about him. Behind the school was a gently sloping hill, a lush green pasture used for grazing sheep which was dotted with fruit trees. If he ran straight up the hill he could dart from tree to tree. But what if he was spotted in between? The higher he went, the easier it would be for the soldiers to see him from down on the street. If he ran to his left, staying low on the edge of the pasture behind his own school and the infant school next door, he could hug the wall and keep out of sight until he picked up the footpath that crossed the corner of the field and led to Rue de la Cimetière, further up towards the edge of the village. Not knowing how many Germans were about, the second option seemed safer to Alfred for now.

Sticking closely to the wall, he began to jog along the edge of the field, parallel with the Peyrilhac road. As he went, his thoughts wandered back to the classroom. Had Monsieur Gravois done a head count? Had the German noticed that he had gone missing from the back of the line? Suddenly worried that he was being followed, Alfred looked back over his shoulder. He didn't see the figure coming out of the garden gate in front of him until it was too late.

Smack! The pair collided. Alfred bounced off the larger man and landed in a pile of old sacks. Temporarily dazed, he expected to hear a German voice ordering him to get up, but instead a floury hand reached out to help him up.

'Sorry, son,' a familiar voice whispered. 'I didn't see you coming.'

It was Benoit Martin, his father's boss from the bakery. Separated from his wife, Benoit had been convinced that, whatever the Germans' reason was for taking the men away from the women and children, it was bad. He had heard all about the Fourniers' experience in Charly from Leon and didn't trust the Germans for a second. So he had taken advantage of a scuffle between one of the soldiers and a group of men who had come into Oradour for the day by tram from Limoges. He had waited until the soldier was surrounded by the men and then darted down an alleyway behind the smithy. From there he had crossed the street and slipped round the back of the Joubert family barn. Then he had crept along the backs of the houses until he had reached the garden of his own cottage on the Peyrilhac road, next to the infant school.

He had intended to hide indoors, perhaps in the loft or in the cellar, but as he had made to open the back door leading into his kitchen, he had heard movement inside. The Germans were searching the rooms, making sure that no one was hiding there. He could hear his furniture being thrown around, his possessions being smashed, cupboard doors being torn open.

As quietly as he could, he had retreated up the garden path and back out of the rear gate. He was planning on carrying on along the field edge until he reached the end of the village. If he could get beyond the road block without being seen, he could run to the next village and get help.

'Why don't you come with me, Monsieur Martin?' Alfred suggested. 'I have a plan. I'm heading for the woods behind the cemetery. That's where my mother and father will be going.'

Benoit was about to explain to Alfred that his mother and father were still in the fairground when he suddenly heard German voices in the garden the other side of the fence. He grabbed Alfred's sleeve and dived with him behind a large sheet of corrugated iron which was leaning up against a compost heap. He held his hand over Alfred's mouth and put his other finger to his own lips, the fear in his own eyes meeting the panic in Alfred's.

Alfred and Benoit clung to one another, trying desperately to control their rapid breathing as they heard the two German voices getting louder. One soldier said something to the other and then laughed nastily. The sound made Alfred's flesh turn cold.

The baker and the boy lay there, in their tiny, pungent hideout, too terrified to move while the two soldiers casually shared a cigarette. Then at last they could hear the sound of their boots retreating up the garden path, and their voices getting quieter as they moved back towards the house.

'We'd better lie low here for a while, Alfie,' Benoit said, wiping the sweat from his eyes with a trembling hand. 'It's too dangerous to move at the moment. Let's wait and see what happens. We're well hidden here.'

Alfred shifted his weight, turning onto his back to make himself a little more comfortable, and wiped his hands on his trousers to remove the gritty earth that clung to his damp palms. As he did so, he thought how his mother would have scolded him had she seen him doing that, how she would have sent him straight to the sink to clean them with soap and water. He wished he could be with her now, and a tear began to trickle down his cheek.

16: THE SEPARATION

SYLVIE WAS terrified. Why had the Germans suddenly decided to separate the men from the women and children? What were they going to do with the men? And what about Christelle, Sabine and Alfred? Were they still safe at school?

Until now, she had felt alone in her terror of the Germans, but as she joined the cluster of anxious women and children being herded over to the left-hand side of the fairground, she could see an increasing sense of panic among the others. The sound of gunshots was getting more frequent and seemed to be coming from all directions now, and even over the increasing noise levels among the crowd in the fairground, they could all hear the occasional scream.

The soldiers, at first calm and composed, were now edgy and becoming increasingly unpleasant as they barked their orders. Without showing any compassion, they cut through the family groups trying to stay huddled together until the last moment, and sorted husband from wife, sister from brother, boy from man. Once divided, the various groups were herded roughly away, hurried along with shouts of '*Vite! Vite!*'

Children, distressed at being separated from their fathers, were starting to wail, and here and there arguments broke out over who should go where or who should stay with whom. Sylvie saw Madame Renard, a teacher from the boys' school, bravely standing up to a stony-faced young officer who was trying to drag her sixteen-year-old son, Pierre, from her arms.

'He is old enough!' shouted the German. 'He goes with the men.'

Pierre's large physical frame masked the intelligence of a small child. His mind was irrevocably damaged by a difficult and traumatic birth. Yet although his tiny premature body had been so tragically starved of oxygen, the baby he grew into was lavished with love. The Renards had never once allowed their son's limitations to spoil his enjoyment of life, and they had come to Oradour believing it to be the perfect place for their son to grow up, a place where he would be valued, welcomed and included in the community. Now Madame Renard was doing what she did best, fighting to protect her son, and even the SS officer seemed to sense the futility of battling against her.

Pierre Renard was the only boy over fifteen who was allowed to stay with his mother.

'Maman! Maman!'

Sylvie nearly collapsed with relief as Christelle and Sabine rushed into her arms. 'Oh, my beautiful girls. My babies.' She kissed them on the tops of their heads and hugged them close. Sabine was shaking like a leaf.

'It's alright now, my darlings. We are together,' Sylvie murmured into their hair, pushing aside her own doubts in order to comfort her children.

'But Maman, we saw such terrible things,' sobbed Christelle. 'An old man, the Germans shot him right there in the street because he couldn't walk fast enough.'

Sylvie tried to quell the panic rising in her throat.

'Girls, where's Alfred?'

Christelle looked about her. 'He's escaped,' she whispered. 'He wouldn't come with us. He wanted to keep our family pact.'

Sylvie felt a rush of longing for her son. Her wonderful, adorable little Alfie. God bless him. For once he had done as he was told.

'Where's Papa?' Sabine suddenly asked, lifting her head from her mother's chest.

'The Germans are making all the men and the older boys line up over there. Look.'

151

On the other side of the fairground, the soldiers were now assembling the men and older boys into some kind of order. They were directing them to sit down on the grass in three lines, facing the wall.

'I don't like this,' Sylvie said shakily. 'I've got to find out what's happening. Christelle, sit with the others.'

Sylvie disentangled herself from her children and cautiously approached the soldier who had agreed to let Pierre stay with his mother. At least she knew he could speak a little French, and she hoped he would be as lenient with her as he had been with Madame Renard. Having finished organising the men and women into groups, he was now standing guard over the women, holding his rifle.

'Excuse me,' Sylvie said quietly. 'Please can you tell me why we have to be separated from our husbands?'

'Major Dietrich's orders,' replied the soldier curtly.

'Yes, of course,' said Sylvie, wondering how far she dare push it. 'But I don't understand why. No one has asked to see our papers yet.'

'Papers are irrelevant now. Something far more important has come up. The Major believes that somewhere in Oradour there's a secret arms store. So we are carrying out a thorough search. It will be better if the women and children wait in the church while that is done.'

'And the men?' enquired Sylvie.

'They are to be questioned.' The soldier leant forwards and leered at Sylvie. He was close enough for her to feel his hot breath on her cheek. 'Now, is there anything else, Madame, or are you satisfied?'

Sylvie started to back away. 'No... I mean, yes. Thank you. Thank you for telling me.'

Sylvie's information seemed to calm some of the women and children around her, but she was still convinced something was very wrong. She had seen something in the soldier's eyes. He had been lying to her.

A sense of dread was rapidly building up inside her, quickening her heartbeat, and when she saw Major Dietrich striding back into the fairground, ready to direct operations once again, her chest clamped in panic and she found it difficult to breathe.

That was when she heard Dietrich giving the order for the women and children to be led away to the church.

This is it, she thought. *We're being taken away so we don't see them all getting shot.*

She made to break out of the line. Dietrich saw her and raised his hand, ready to strike, but Christelle caught the back of her dress and pulled her back.

'No, Maman! They will kill you if you cause trouble, like that poor old man!'

Sylvie looked into her daughter's eyes. Her heart was breaking but she knew that Christelle was right.

'When did you get so grown up?' she said, framing Christelle's beautiful oval face with her hands. 'Your father would be so proud of you.'

Gripping one another's hands, Sylvie and Christelle slipped back into line behind Sabine, Louis and Paulette, and the long line of women and children began to file out of the fairground, frantically scanning the rows of men as they went, in the hope of making reassuring eye contact with their husbands and sons.

Sylvie spotted Leon. He was sitting in the middle of the three rows next to Dr Depaul, his shoulders slumped, resting his forehead in his hands. She willed him to raise his head, for his eyes to meet hers, but he was too lost in his thoughts, in his desperation. As she turned the corner and left the fairground, she saw her husband's shoulders beginning to shake.

'*Au revoir, Papa!*' Paulette called out cheerfully, walking backwards so that she could wave to her father as she left.

Watching the little girl waving so pathetically to her father, Major Dietrich sniggered. Of course, the father wasn't even looking. How naïve she was to expect him to care. But then, this whole village seemed ridiculously naïve. They had been so easy to convince, so quick to comply, and he despised them for hanging onto every word of their foolish, jumped-up fat cat of a mayor. What good had that done them? Did they really think that all this was just about a search for weapons, or that an SS commander of his experience really believed they had the capability to hide someone like Thomas Klausner in their pitiable little village? Good God, how he hated everything about these people and their insignificant, cosy lives. He didn't care if they were innocent.

PART 5

SATURDAY 10 JUNE, 1944 (LATE AFTERNOON)

17: TO THE CHURCH

SUNDAY 11 June 1944 was meant to be a day of celebration in Oradour. The Corpus Christi procession was all planned and the whole village had been looking forward to the festivities.

After the Mass, the consecrated water that represented Christ's sacrifice was to be carried through the streets on a cart, shaded from the sun by an elaborate canopy as it wound its way round the village.

Accompanying the priests, who carried banners dedicated to their patron saints, would be the children, dressed in their best clothes and bearing their colourful flower garlands.

The procession which now wound its way through Oradour to the church was far from cheerful, and the drained, pale complexions of the frightened women and children were a stark contrast to the gaudy reds, pinks and purples of the decorative flowers which lined their route.

Not wanting to invite any trouble from their grave-faced guards, the group had at first fallen into an accepting silence, broken only now and then by a muffled whimper or the kind of involuntary sniff that follows an outburst of tears, and which was framed by the clunking of the children's wooden-soled clogs, as they trudged out of the fairground, past the well, and down Rue de la Cimetière. But after a short distance, one of the soldiers ordered the children to sing a song.

'It will cheer everyone up,' he laughed.

A few worried little voices struck up the first few lines of the hymn they had been practising for the Mass the next day, but the children's enthusiasm soon waned, their voices trailed off, and silence descended once again on the procession.

The homes they passed were eerily empty. Doors and windows hung open, shops were deserted, customers long gone. As she passed the cobbler's store, Sylvie remembered the last time she had been in there, just a few days ago, to buy new clogs for Louis. He had been growing so quickly since his fourth birthday and it seemed only five minutes since he had needed his last pair. Monsieur Babin had been so kind. He knew Sylvie and Leon hadn't got much money and had pretended the clogs were on sale so as not to embarrass her by offering her any charity. Gratefully, she had bought the shoes at the discount price, but had asked Leon to make sure he gave the cobbler the biggest loaf of bread on the shelf the next time he came into the bakery.

They soon reached the church, where Audrey Rousseau had been arranging flowers earlier. Half-trimmed flowers and pieces of ribbon were scattered along the pews as they filed inside, and the first few women to enter had to move aside several buckets of blooms to make room for their prams.

'Be careful with those,' screeched Audrey, as she rushed over to pick up a bucket of white roses which had been knocked over, spilling water across the stone flagstones. 'Those are from the Mayor's garden!'

The young mother who had caused the accident looked at her incredulously. 'I hardly think a bit of spilled water and a few scattered petals matter now, do they?' she snapped. 'My baby is only seven months old. What's going to happen to him? He doesn't need to hear you shouting!'

Sylvie, who had just come through the door with her four children, felt sorry for Audrey and went to take her hand. She knew that the other woman's outburst was just a reaction to the dreadful situation they were all in. She smiled at the young mother and took Audrey to one side.

'It's all right, Audrey,' she said comfortingly. 'I'll help you tidy all this up later, when the Germans have gone. We'll finish the flowers together as we'd planned. When we've done, the church will be more beautiful than it's ever been before.'

'Thank you, Sylvie,' said Audrey, smiling weakly. 'You are a good friend.'

Sylvie watched Audrey joining her teenage daughter, Alita, in one of the stalls at the front usually reserved for the choir. How she wished that what she had said were true, that she and Audrey could finish the afternoon arranging flowers. In truth, she doubted that they would even see the end of the afternoon, but she knew she had to keep some hope alive. She had to stay focused and keep her mind on practical things, on ways to keep the children safe, on looking for opportunities to escape.

Audrey was probably wise to grab a seat now, she thought, as the church filled up rapidly behind them. There were already hundreds of women and children inside with many more still crowded on the gravelled yard, being ushered in by the SS troops like guests at a macabre wedding.

Finding a quiet corner by the altar, Sylvie and the children crouched down and sat on the cold stone floor. She looked up to the high vaulted ceiling, dappled with the sunlight that filtered through the tall, arched windows above the altar and, not for the first time that day, Sylvie began to pray.

As he lay flat on his back, sandwiched in the cramped and musty gap between Benoit's sweaty body and the hard, ridged corrugated iron which formed their shelter, Alfred looked up at the narrow shafts of sunlight beaming through the tiny holes in the metal. He could see specks of dust floating about, caught in the sunbeam, and he watched as they danced around when he blew gently upwards.

He had lost track of how long he and Benoit had been lying there, but he guessed it had to be well over half an hour. A couple of times he had whispered to Benoit to ask if he thought it was safe to move, but the baker had shaken his head, replying that he could still hear too much movement out there in the streets.

Alfred had strained his ears to listen, too. Benoit was right, there was still a lot of shouting – all in

German, which he couldn't understand – and now he could hear a lot of marching, too. In fact it sounded like hundreds of people, walking away from where he and Benoit hid, not closer… and they were moving slowly, rhythmically, wooden shoes tapping on the cobbles like the gentle beat of a funeral drum.

Now and again he could hear an outbreak of singing. Children's voices. They would burst into song and then gradually trail off, as if they kept forgetting the words.

Alfred could hear dogs barking in the distance, too, and his thoughts turned to Bobby. He prayed that the little dog was staying out of trouble. Hopefully he would be reunited safely with Patric by now, basking in a successful mission to clinch the deal on Philippe's marriage proposal to Nadia.

Alfred suddenly felt stifled, stuck there in hiding. He wanted to keep moving. He needed to find his family and he was sure they would be on their way to the cemetery by now.

He made up his mind. He would listen out for a sign, something which told him it was safe – or the right time – to make his move. Then he would be off, with or without Benoit.

18: TO THE BARNS

LEON WAS distraught. As he dropped to the ground to take his place in the row of men, all forced to sit facing the north wall like a gang of condemned criminals, he put his head in his hands. He felt ashamed.

How could he have been so naïve as to think that he and Sylvie and the children could sneak off from the fairground? How could he have let his family down so badly with such a pathetic, desperate plan?

He had failed. Failed to protect his family. Failed to listen to Sylvie. He had no one but himself to blame. He had become too content in Oradour, trusting and complacent. He hadn't wanted to believe that their perfect life in Oradour could ever change, and so he had refused to listen to Sylvie or his own conscience, and refused to believe that they were in trouble. And now he had put all his family in danger. All except Alfred.

Leon wondered what had happened to his son. As he had been standing there just now in the crowd with the rest of the men, he had seen Christelle and Sabine running to Sylvie and the little ones on the other side of the fairground. But there was no sign of Alfred.

There had been gunshots. Had Alfred been killed? Leon had tried to read his wife's expression, but it was so hard to see her face clearly from where he stood. He could see her hugging the girls, kissing their hair. But he couldn't be sure whether Christelle and Sabine had brought good news or bad.

Yet somehow, something told Leon that his son was still alive. Alfred knew the streets and fields around Oradour better than anyone else thanks to all his adventures. He spent hours out and about with that little dog of Patric's. If anyone was going to escape from these Germans, it would be Alfie. Leon smiled. He would be willing to bet that the little rascal was there in the woods behind the cemetery right now, waiting for them.

And it was that image that stayed with Leon as he sat there facing the wall. Little Alfred, sitting on the ground at the foot of his favourite tree – the one with the hole in it, big enough to climb in. What if they never reached him? How long would he wait?

As he pictured his son's earnest face, his gorgeous floppy red hair, Leon lowered his head so that no one could see the tears fall from his downcast eyes.

'That's it, then. They've gone,' said Bertrand Depaul, who had found a place in the line next to him. 'Do you think we'll ever see them again?'

Leon looked up in dismay. He had been so lost in his own thoughts and misery that he had failed to see the last few women and children being led out of the fairground. He had missed Sylvie. He hoped she had not seen him sitting there feeling so sorry for himself.

'God only knows, Doctor. But it's not looking good.'

Major Dietrich, who had been directing the exodus of women and children, now crossed the fairground and began walking up and down the lines of men, staring at them with a disturbing hunger in his eyes.

Is this the moment? thought Leon. *Do they shoot us all now? Is this how it ends?*

After a few moments of icy silence in which no one dared meet Dietrich's gaze, the Major began to speak, pausing after each sentence for his interpreter to make his meaning absolutely clear.

'Your women and children have been taken to the church where they will remain until we have finished our search of the village.'

There was a ripple of relief along the line. Their wives, mothers, sisters and children would be safe.

'Now, I am going to give you all one last chance to tell me if you know anything about the kidnap of Major

Thomas Klausner or if you have any information about weapons being stored secretly here in Oradour.'

Dietrich continued to walk up and down menacingly along the lines of men. He reached Henri Depaul, who was sitting rather awkwardly on his briefcase at the far end of Leon's row, his legs crossed uncomfortably beneath him. Dietrich stopped, turned, and suddenly kicked the Mayor's briefcase out from underneath him so that he tumbled backwards onto the ground, covering his suit with dust and bits of grass.

Automatically, Denis Babin, who was sitting next to the Mayor, reached out to help his neighbour, but Dietrich screamed out, '*Lass ihn!* Leave him! He will sit on the earth like the rest of you.'

Henri's face was red with anger and humiliation. 'We have nothing to say to you, Major,' he said through gritted teeth. 'As I stated before, we have nothing to hide here.'

'So you say.'

Dietrich smirked then turned and beckoned six of his officers to join him in front of the bewildered men.

'We are going to teach you all a very important lesson about the SS. You see, we always do our job properly. By the time we leave this village, we will have combed every inch of every building and we will leave nothing – absolutely nothing – behind.'

While the men sat in silence, Dietrich divided the three rows of men into six groups of various sizes, ranging from twenty to sixty men, and assigned one officer to each group. He then gave each officer a map with one of six sites carefully marked upon it. Then he addressed the civilians collectively for one last time.

'While we carry out our search, you are to be taken to six different locations. One of my men will lead each group of you and you will be closely watched at all times. So don't try anything stupid. Anyone who tries to escape will be shot.'

With that, Dietrich stepped backwards and folded his arms, content to watch his master plan being put into action.

One by one, the SS officers ordered their groups of men to get to their feet. As they stood, each bewildered crowd of captives was surrounded by soldiers who proceeded to kick, prod and poke them like cattle as they herded them away.

The elderly grandfather of Philippe, a farmer like his son and grandson, was too slow for one SS officer's liking and received a kick in the leg. He stumbled forwards, crying out with pain, and the group had to close around him to allow Philippe and his father to lift and support him, one arm around each of their shoulders, so that he could carry on.

Two of the groups were taken off to the west, towards the hotel and the Rue Depaul. The first stop was the wine store, owned by Alfred's friend Monsieur Demarais. The SS leader entered first, violently kicking over a stack of wine crates with his boot to make room for his twenty-five prisoners, among them the Mayor. Dozens of bottles of Monsieur Demarais' precious wine toppled to the floor, adding a menacing glitter of splinters to the spilled blood-red liquid.

The second group of men, including Patric Depaul, was taken further down the road past the girls' school, and Patric watched in horror as the soldiers fired at the lock and broke open the doors to his own garage. Buffeted along by the rest of the group, he was shoved through the archway, past the old Fiat which he had been working on so lovingly to restore, and out into the back yard, well away from any tools which could be turned into weapons.

Patric was trembling, more out of anger than fear, and he had to clench his fists and dig his fingernails into his palms to stop himself from screaming out at the injustice of it all. He wanted to charge at the Germans and fight back, but he knew that he had no chance against men with machine guns and rifles. He could end up getting not only himself killed, but the others, too. For now, he would have to stay quiet and endure the agony of seeing his premises, his own little empire of which he was so proud, invaded.

The remaining groups of men were taken out of the other end of the fairground past the well, following in the footsteps of the women and children. The first group to be led away had the furthest to go. They were taken down the hill beyond the church to an isolated barn near the river, belonging to the water mill. The next group, which included Doctor Bertrand Depaul and twenty-four others, was taken to the smithy. Leon had told Bertrand that Monsieur Lefevre had escaped and, as he was thrust inside, Bertrand realised how wise the young smith had been in his decision to flee. For, as his eyes grew accustomed to the darkness inside the workshop, he recoiled in shock.

There, left in a heap in the middle of the floor, their bicycles thrown on top of them like rubbish waiting to be collected, were the bodies of the five young tourists. As the meaning of what they saw sank in, the men in the smithy began to panic, turning to try to force their way back out, but the heavy wooden doors were rapidly bolted, condemning them to darkness with no means of escape.

The final groups of men were shepherded into two barns – one, the Masson barn, on the corner of Rue de la Cimetière and the other nearer the church, on the main road out to Limoges, belonging to Denis Babin, the clog-maker. The larger of the two barns was owned by Monsieur Joubert, a local farmer, and this was where Leon Fournier and his next-door neighbour, Guy Dupont, found themselves along with about sixty others. Although the barn was the largest in Oradour, bales of hay were stacked up along three of the walls, and the centre space was filled with Monsieur Joubert's selection of farm carts. Seeing the lack of room inside, one of the SS soldiers ordered Leon and six other men to drag the carts out into the street, clearing a passageway into the middle of the barn. While they did so, two other soldiers began sweeping the floor at the entrance to the barn. At first, Leon was surprised to see them helping, but his surprise turned to concern when the two soldiers then began setting up their machine guns on the freshly-cleared ground.

With a small space cleared, the rest of the men were directed to enter the barn where, squashed into an anxious huddle, they watched helplessly as the two machine gunners turned their barrels to point menacingly at them. They were trapped like bees in a honeypot.

A nervous hush descended on the barn as, one by one, conversations between the men died away into silence.

Dietrich's plan had placed all six groups of men in locations out of direct line of sight of one another. Had they been able to see where the others were being kept, Leon and his fellow prisoners would have realised that they were all in the same predicament. Stationed outside the Masson barn, the mill owner's barn, the garage, the wine store and the smithy were similar machine gun posts, each backed up by five or six other soldiers carrying rifles or hand-held machine guns, their ammunition belts coiled expectantly around their shoulders.

Huddled together in their makeshift prisons, throats and mouths dry, and with fear exuding from every pore in the suffocating heat, all the men could do was wait, and hope.

For now, Oradour was quiet.

19: THE EXPLOSION

AS HE watched the last few prisoners being led out of the fairground, Dietrich calmly leant back on the cool stone of the village well, and reached into the inside pocket of his jacket. He tipped a cigarette out of its slightly crumpled packet and put it into his mouth. Then he took out a matchbox from his trouser pocket, picked out a match and struck it on the side of the well. He lit his cigarette, drew on it deeply and blew out a long, slow stream of smoke, watching it dissipate into the warm afternoon air.

So far, all had gone smoothly and he knew that in less than a couple more hours, it would all be over. He could be back in Limoges before six, sharing his success with Major General Scholz. The thought brought delicious goosebumps to the surface of his skin, and the pleasure this gave him, combined with the sudden rush of nicotine through his veins, made him feel distinctly light-headed.

He surveyed the empty fairground and considered his next move. His men needed time to move their prisoners, but the plan was well on track, so he still had time to visit all six target locations on his way to the church. He checked his watch. 3.45. Perfect.

Dietrich took one last drag on his cigarette then threw it to the floor, grinding the stub into the dirt with his foot. Then he adjusted his cap and swaggered off in the direction of the wine store.

There was shouting coming from the Hotel de la Glane, and as Dietrich cut across the terrace he saw two soldiers dragging a woman and two young girls out through the glass doors. Seeing Major Dietrich, the soldiers stopped in their tracks.

'We found them hiding in the cellar, Major. They're Jews. They were too spineless to come to the fairground. We were going to take them to the church.'

'It's too far,' said Dietrich, taking out his revolver. 'There isn't time. They can come with me.'

He took hold of the woman by the arm and shoved her in front of him.

'Walk! All of you!' he shouted, and marched them across the road. 'Tell her to be quiet!' he screamed at the mother, as the younger daughter started to cry loudly.

At the entrance to the wine store, Dietrich ordered the woman and the two girls to go inside and join the men. Standing between the two machine guns, he stood and briefly surveyed the prisoners, meeting the hate-fuelled gaze of Henri Depaul, still clutching his now scratched and dusty briefcase, waiting there to hear his fate with the rest of the terrified group. Looking directly into the Mayor's eyes, Dietrich spoke calmly to the machine gunner at his side. 'I want the woman and her brats kept at the front. Make sure they are the first to fall.'

Then he turned his back and walked away, ignoring the cries of outrage and the wailing of a mother in despair.

After the wine store, Dietrich visited all five other locations, finishing up at the small barn by the mill. At each post, he conferred with his men, made sure that their orders were clearly understood, and checked that the machine guns had been set up as planned. Content that everything was well under control, he reminded his troops to stay calm and wait for the signal.

It was time to head back up the hill to the church.

As he came round the end of the wall and climbed up the gravel drive into the churchyard, Dietrich was pleased to see that the church doors were already closed. Clearly all the women and children were secure inside and his men were guarding all the exits.

'How many are there?' he asked the officer who greeted him.

'Well over four hundred, we reckon, maybe four hundred and fifty,' the officer replied nervously. 'Major... are you sure this is the right thing to do? There are so many of them.'

Immediately he regretted asking, as a look of rage swept over Dietrich's face. 'Are you telling me you wish to be relieved of your duty?' he enquired, fingering the butt of his revolver as it rested in its holster at his hip.

'No, Major. Not at all,' answered the officer quickly. 'I was just checking there had been no change of plan.'

'Of course not!' snapped Dietrich. 'Now get back to your post.'

Dietrich swung away from the shamefaced officer then crossed the yard to a parked truck, guarded by its own small platoon. This was the truck which his driver, Ragnar, had observed being loaded up secretly back in Saint Junien.

After a few brief words from Dietrich, the platoon began carefully unloading a crate holding one of the mysterious packages from the back of the truck. When they had finished, Dietrich gave them a salute. It was the signal that they could move in.

They knew exactly what to do.

Sitting at the side of the nave near the choir, Sylvie and the children waited patiently. Sabine had pulled a piece of string from her pocket and was keeping Louis and Paulette entertained by showing them how to play cat's cradle. Christelle sat a few inches apart, her back to the wall, staring out in front of her and saying nothing. Sylvie reached for her hand and gave it a squeeze. She couldn't bear to think about the scenes her daughter had just witnessed and as she looked at the troubled young face she felt the anger welling up inside her.

Although it was relatively calm now inside the church, there were so many people crammed into the pews and into every alcove that it was hard to keep track of any noises coming from outside. Every time Sylvie thought she could hear something, a baby would cry, a child would cough or one of the women would shift about, trying to find some comfort on her hard wooden seat or stony floor.

Every so often Sylvie would catch Audrey's eye and the two women would swap comforting glances, a consoling exchange of sympathy, affection and mutual support.

Sylvie glanced at her watch. It was four o'clock. Normally the church bells hanging high up in the tower above her would be rung every hour to broadcast the time all over Oradour. Today the big bronze bells remained motionless and silent, as if time had been forced to stand still.

A moment later, the front door of the church opened and in came two young soldiers, aged about twenty Sylvie guessed, gingerly carrying a rough wooden crate.

'Make way!' they shouted, as they forced a path up the aisle through the tightly packed crowd of women and children and placed the box on the altar.

'Oh my God,' mumbled Sylvie. From where she sat she could see both sides of the altar, and her sharp eyes did not miss the long wires which trailed down from the back of the crate and onto the floor.

She glanced at Audrey who was staring at the soldiers, her mouth open in horror. She had seen the wires too.

Sylvie didn't realise that the long piercing scream which then rose and filled the air in the nave was her own. Somehow, she felt disconnected from herself. It was as if she was watching the soldiers preparing the detonator fuses from outside her own body, and it must have been someone else, someone too desperate and too hopeless to be her, who threw herself at the German soldier as he turned, ready to run past him, to flee from the death-trap he had just created. But she was aware of him pushing her off, she saw him raising his arm, and she felt the bullet thump into her chest. And as she fell crashing down, she knew that the blood which began to flow onto the cold stone floor was hers.

Her children had no time to help her, no chance to say goodbye to their mother, because it was then that the bomb went off.

The explosion was met with screams of terror from the women and children who weren't immediately killed. Acrid, black smoke filled their eyes, noses and throats. In a wild panic, everyone who could still move rushed to find a corner, a space, where they could breathe clean air, but there were too few safe places left, and hundreds were unable to escape the choking fumes, which left them coughing and spluttering for breath.

Every door was suddenly pressed with bodies, desperately trying to break the locks and force their way out. Audrey and her daughter Alita were hammering on the door which led to the sacristy, where the priests and the altar boys normally dressed themselves for Mass. More and more desperate women were gathering behind them and for a moment Audrey thought they might be crushed by the weight of the people shoving them against the heavy oak door. Then suddenly the door's rusty old hinges gave way and the terrified crowd surged through into the room, which was usually off limits to women. Audrey had to fight her way to her feet and pull Alita up to prevent her from being trampled.

She saw Christelle and Sabine, shocked and dazed, staggering through the doorway, each struggling to carry one of their two younger siblings. Paulette was screaming, the tears leaving white streaks down her smoke-blackened face. In her panic she was half-choking Sabine, so tightly had she wrapped her tiny arms around her big sister's neck. Louis's little body hung limply in Christelle's arms.

Then the gunfire started. Under the cover of the smoke bomb, the German soldiers had poured in through the front door and were now spraying the nave with bullets.

The breakout into the sacristy had not gone unnoticed, and it was here that the soldiers went next. Trapped there in the small room, the women and children were sitting ducks. Christelle, still clutching her brother's body, was among the first to fall. Sabine spun round, trying to protect Paulette by throwing herself down on top of her on the cold hard floor. It did no good.

Audrey and Alita were the furthest into the room and, as the soldiers opened fire, they began darting here and there behind the rest of the women, trying madly to find something or someone to shelter behind. But the room was sparsely furnished and, as the women and children in front of them began to fall, there was little left to shield them.

'Get down,' Audrey whispered to Alita, pulling her to the ground. As the defenceless figures dropped all around them, Audrey and Alita closed their eyes and waited. Audrey was holding on tightly to Alita's hand, so she felt the jerk as her daughter's body was struck, felt the muscles in her fingers contract, and then go slack. Audrey fought back the urge to scream.

But then, as suddenly as they had come in, the soldiers pulled out of the church, and the devastating sound of gunfire was replaced by the moans of the injured and the dying, and the cries of those, like Audrey, who had seen their loved ones mown down in front of their eyes.

From where she lay, frozen with grief in the sacristy, clinging onto her daughter's hand, Audrey could not see what was happening in the nave. But she could hear the booted feet of the soldiers moving around. It sounded like they were shifting furniture, scraping and dragging heavy things across the floor.

Suddenly she felt a hand tapping on her leg. The young mother whom she had scolded when they first arrived, clutching her baby to her breast, was gesturing towards the door.

'We've got to get out,' she mouthed. 'They are going to burn us.'

Audrey shook her head, the tears sliding down her cheeks. She didn't want to leave Alita alone.

'She's gone,' whispered the young mother, realising Audrey's dilemma. 'There's nothing you can do for her. Save yourself. Please. Please help me save my baby!'

This last plea finally sparked Audrey's resolve. She knew she had to try. For Alita, for Sylvie, Christelle, Sabine and the little ones, she had to prove that life was worth fighting for, that she would never give up.

She nodded to the girl and turned to gaze for one last time at her precious daughter, her face so familiar, so perfect and yet now so still. Raising herself up, Audrey bent gently over her daughter's body, taking care not to move or disturb her, unable to believe that she couldn't possibly hurt her any more, and softly kissed her on the forehead.

As her tears fell onto Alita's cheeks she brought her hand down across her face and closed her eyes.

'Goodnight my princess,' she whispered. 'Sleep tight.'

Then Audrey Rousseau took a deep breath and got slowly, cautiously to her feet. She had a job to do.

Audrey gestured silently to the young mother to follow her and together they tip-toed quietly over and around the fallen bodies, until they reached the door back into the nave. They pressed themselves flat up against the wall and Audrey peered round into the main body of the church. It was still dark and full of thick black smoke, but framed in the daylight shining through the front door opposite, Audrey could just make out the shape of soldiers moving around. They were wearing gas masks to protect themselves from the fumes and were throwing objects – straw, firewood, broken chairs, bits of splintered church pews – into the centre aisle.

She glanced back at her new companion and down at the woman's baby, which was bound to her chest in a sling. If the baby cried, the cover of the smoke would not be enough. They had to move fast.

Audrey waited until there was a pause in the movement of the soldiers across the nave and then tugged at the mother's arm, indicating that she should copy her and remove her shoes, then get ready to go.

Using their sleeves to keep the foul-smelling fumes from their mouths and noses, the two women sprinted, hidden by the smoke, back up to the altar. Above it were three tall windows, all of which had been shattered by the bomb blast. The middle window was large enough to squeeze through.

While the mother crouched with her baby behind the damaged altar, Audrey found the stool which she had been using earlier that day to stand on when she was decorating the windowsills with flowers. It had been thrown across the choir by the blast but, amazingly, was still in one piece. Now she propped it up against the wall below the middle window and, swallowing hard to quell her urge to cough as the smoke stung her throat, she climbed up onto it and reached up.

Audrey was not an especially fit woman, but at that moment she found strength she never knew she had, for somehow she managed to heave herself up, her bare feet scraping up the wall to get a grip, and threw herself out through the gap.

The window was a good three metres above the ground outside and, although there was a shrubbery to break her fall, Audrey was momentarily winded from the landing. She sat there among the plants for a few seconds, trying to get her breath, gulping in the fresh air. Then she heard the baby's screams above her.

Rapidly she got to her feet. The desperate young mother was hanging half in and half out of the window, her baby dangling down awkwardly from her sling.

'Catch her,' she cried. 'Quickly, they've spotted us.'

Audrey got ready to catch the tiny screaming bundle but there was no time. Alerted by the baby's cries, one of the soldiers had rushed across the nave. He leapt up onto the stool and just missed grabbing the mother's back foot as she jumped out, her baby nearly falling from her arms.

They started to run, but the soldier had already aimed his gun. The mother and baby fell just a few metres from the window. Five bullets thudded into Audrey and, as she collapsed, she rolled down the steep bank which led down from the back of the church to the retaining wall.

Satisfied, the soldier climbed down from the window and went back to work in the nave.

Following their orders to finish off the job, the soldiers set light to the bonfire they had created in the church. When they had finished piling up as much combustible material as they could find to hand, they took up their weapons and opened fire once again, trying to silence the last few cries and groans. Then, at the platoon leader's signal, they lowered their guns and paused before exiting to toss some grenades into the pile.

Then the front door was pulled close and bolted shut.

When Audrey came round, lying there in the ditch by the church wall, the first thing that struck her was the smell. The sweet, sickly smell of burning flesh mixed with thick, suffocating wood smoke.

Then the pain hit her. It felt like there was a knife being driven through her shoulder, and both her legs felt like they had been hit with a steam roller. But she knew she had to get away. She could be seen and it wouldn't take the soldiers long to realise she was alive.

Mustering all her strength, she started to crawl on her stomach, dragging her injured legs through the grass until she reached a gap in the wall leading to the church garden. Centimetre by centimetre she edged her way into the garden and dug herself into the soft earth between some rows of peas. Finally, satisfied that she was well hidden, and utterly exhausted, she passed out.

Once the grenades exploded, the bonfire piled up in the nave took only seconds to ignite. The dry straw and kindling and broken wooden furniture burned rapidly and, fuelled by hundreds of burning bodies, the flames were soon soaring upwards, hungrily licking the church roof.

Fed by the air being sucked through the broken windows, the church turned into a raging inferno, high enough to burn through the roof timbers, savage enough to reach up inside the bell-rope tower, and hot enough to melt the huge bronze bells.

In just over an hour, Oradour's beloved church had been transformed into a burnt-out, smouldering shell. Apart from Audrey Rousseau, not one of its reluctant congregation that day got out alive.

20: THE CORNFIELD

FROM THEIR tiny hideout beside the compost heap, Alfred and Benoit heard the explosion inside the church. They had fallen silent, too traumatised to talk and too scared of being discovered to make any noise. Alfred had even closed his eyes for a while. He had grown bored of staring up at the corrugated roof and, after the adrenaline rush of his escape from the schoolroom, he was starting to feel fatigued. Perhaps if he could just rest a little, it would help to pass the time…

But then the blast from the church shook the ground beneath him and rocked him back to his senses. His eyelids flew open.Simultaneously, Benoit shot up onto his elbows. 'What the hell was that?' he whispered.

'It sounded like a bomb.'

'I think it was. From the church, do you think?'

'Yes, it sounded like it.'

'That was the direction all those footsteps were going in... the children's voices… I…'

Benoit didn't finish his sentence because the sound of the explosion was then followed by the chilling sound of gunfire. Repeated shots and machine guns.

Alfred immediately started to shuffle his small body out of the shelter. He was scared. Very scared.

'Where are you going?' cried Benoit, trying to keep his voice low.

'I'm not stopping here any longer,' whispered Alfred, trembling. 'I have to go. I have to get to the cemetery now. Then, if it's clear, I can make it to the woods.'

Alfred was already on his hands and knees, ready to crawl out of the shelter.

'No, Alfie!' Benoit cried, his muted voice straining, too afraid to shout. He reached sideways and grabbed Alfred's ankle, desperate to restrain him, convinced the boy was going to his death. But Alfred was too determined and too terrified to be held back. He shook his foot hard and wriggled free of Benoit's grasp.

Alfred didn't dare glance around him and he didn't want to look back. He simply set his eyes on the opposite side of the field, where he could pick up the little lane which joined onto Rue de la Cimetière, and ran.

There was a footpath diagonally across the field and, for the first forty to fifty metres, Alfred stuck to that, making good speed on the sun-baked, hard trodden earth. He could see the gate now, where the footpath came out onto the lane next to the stonemason's workshop. He was nearly there. But then he heard more gunfire. It seemed to be coming from all directions now, around the village. One minute there was a burst of noise from the direction of the mill, by the river, then it was joined by more distant gunshots, from the far side of the village, back in the direction of his cottage. Alfred tried not to think about what that could mean.

Unsure what to do next, Alfred stopped in the middle of the path and looked wildly about him. Suddenly, taking the lane onto Rue de la Cimetière didn't seem like such a good idea. He was far more likely to run into some soldiers there. In a panic, Alfred turned away from the noise and began running up the hill through the long grass towards the edge of Pierre Petit's cornfield.

More gunfire. Louder now, and much, much closer. It seemed to be coming from the Joubert barn behind him on the corner of Rue de la Cimetière and Rue Depaul. Terrified, Alfred ran head-long into the corn, which in the early summer sun was already as high as his waist. Then he dived down to the ground, taking cover among the thick green shoots. He knew he had to stop. If the Germans were that close they could easily spot him. He had no choice but to wait, to lie low, hidden among the corn, until the firing stopped.

21: ESCAPE FROM THE BARN

THE DEAFENING crack of the explosion inside the church sent shivers up Dietrich's spine. This was the signal he had asked all the platoons at the six locations around the village to listen out for. There was no turning back now. The massacre had begun.

He did not open his mind to the horror of what he was about to cause. He did not see these victims as people. They were purely pawns in the game of war – a game in which he was well practised, and which he could not lose.

He knew that some of his comrades, Captain Krüger and Ragnar among them, thought he was taking a risk in changing Major General Scholz's orders, but he hadn't really *changed* them, he felt. He had adapted them. Improved them. He had reacted to new information and moulded the plan into sheer perfection. No one could deny he was the creator of the greatest strike at the Resistance yet.

After waiting for a few seconds to allow the smoke bomb to fill the nave, Dietrich gave the order for his soldiers to storm in and open fire. The black smoke which billowed out of the door as the men wrenched it open mingled with the sounds of the chaos inside.

'Quick! Quick!' Dietrich roared at his men. The sooner they could shut up that pathetic shouting and screaming, the better.

He watched the soldiers disappearing into the gloom. Then, satisfied that his orders would be carried out as he wished, he passed back control to the platoon leader. He needed to move on. He needed to make sure that the gunfire he could hear from around the village meant that his grisly game was being played out.

Dietrich stayed only a few minutes at the mill barn. All the men inside were dead and the soldiers had begun piling straw and wood on top of the bodies, ready to set them alight. Likewise the men in the barn further up the road, and in the blacksmith's workshop. So far so good.

He walked on up the hill, heading next for the Joubert barn. Near to the junction with Rue de la Cimetière, Dietrich heard a commotion in one of the terraced houses to his left. The troops who were not assigned to the church or to one of the six other key targets around the village had been ordered to continue checking the rest of the buildings for fugitives, then to set fire to each building once it was confirmed as clear.

He ducked his head inside the doorway. It was a tiny, modest home, with a long narrow hallway and just two rooms leading off it. A blond-haired teenage SS soldier was standing blocking the far end of the hallway, near the bottom of the stairs. He was pointing his rifle into a tiny cubby hole under the stairs and shrieking, 'Out! Out!'

'Who's in there?'

The soldier jumped, alarmed at Dietrich's voice.

'Just shoot them, you fool!'

'I, I can't, Major. They're…'

Dietrich had no time for this. He stormed down the hall, taking his revolver from its holster and pulled the soldier out of the way. Cowering in the cramped little cupboard was an old couple, the man shielding his wife's head with his hands.

'Please,' begged the old man, his voice barely audible.

Dietrich fired two shots and put his revolver back in its holster. Without a trace of emotion on his face, he stepped back and slammed the cupboard door shut.

He looked at the young officer, who was leaning with his back against the wall and snivelling, with complete disgust. He began to march back down the hallway towards the front door, but as he drew level with the soldier, he turned and shoved his face into his, their noses almost touching.

The soldier felt Dietrich pressing something into his chest. He was convinced he was about to die too.

Dietrich glanced up at the Death's Head badge on the soldier's cap. 'You don't deserve to wear that badge,' he sneered. 'You're pathetic. I should shoot you, too, for disobeying my orders.'

A trickle of sweat ran down the side of the young soldier's face and his lips trembled.

'Now, can you manage to torch the place, or do I have to do that for you as well?' continued Dietrich, the sarcasm dripping from his every word.

The soldier rapidly nodded his head, his knees weak, and with one last sneer, Dietrich was gone, letting the box of matches that he had been pressing into the soldier's chest fall from his fingers onto Ethan and Rachael's floor.

At the Joubert barn, Leon and the others had been trying to stay calm, despite the machine guns pointing at them from the barn door. The soldiers outside certainly seemed relaxed. They were laughing and joking and Leon began to allow himself to believe the story they had been fed. Maybe Major Dietrich had been telling the truth. Perhaps they were just keeping the men there while they searched the town one last time. If the Germans turned up no evidence, proved that the Mayor was right to say that they were innocent, maybe they would be released.

But then came the explosion from the church. Leon's first thought was of Sylvie and the children. 'Oh my God,' he cried out aloud. 'My family's in there.'

He turned to Guy, who was standing next to him, looking alarmed, his hands above his head.

'What are you doing?' Leon asked, not understanding.

Without taking down his hands, Guy nodded his head towards the barn entrance.

Leon turned and looked straight down the barrel of one of the two machine guns, now being made ready to fire. He opened his mouth, and the last thing he noticed before the bullets started to fly, was that the guns seemed to be aimed rather low.

The initial blast of bullets which sprayed into the crowd of sixty terrified men huddled together in the Joubert barn all came in below waist level. Crying out with pain, one man after the next fell to the floor, clutching at their legs.

Next to Leon, Guy had been hit by a bullet in the

wrist as he gave up his sign of surrender and dived to the ground. Untouched, Leon dropped behind him onto the floor, face down, and was rapidly hidden by falling bodies.

The shooting continued until all sixty men were felled.

'Why are they doing this?' Leon kept asking himself. 'Why aim to wound, not kill?'

When finally the firing stopped, Leon dared to lift his head. Through the tangle of bodies he could just see the machine gunners standing up and lifting their guns to one side. Then the cruel reality of the SS plan hit home.

Two soldiers entered the barn and began scattering straw and firewood then covering it with oil. Meanwhile, the remaining soldiers from the platoon, some carrying rifles, others revolvers, picked their way through the heap of bodies, shooting anyone they thought had remained unscathed.

Leon felt a boot pressing down on his back and had to hold his breath so as not to cry out.

Diving for cover, one man had fallen across Guy Dupont's legs. Guy glanced down and recognised him as an old friend named Gerard, someone he had grown up with. One of the SS officers saw Gerard, too, and saw that he was unhurt. He killed him with a shot to the head, and Guy cried out as he felt the bullet pass through his friend into his own thigh.

More shots were fired. The body in front of Leon went limp. He was certain that he would be next, but his own body was so deeply buried under others that the soldiers did not see that he was still unmarked.

When the soldiers were satisfied that no one could move, they ignited the bonfire that they had created.

Trapped beneath the weight of the bodies above them, Guy and Leon could feel the fire beginning to singe their clothes. Guy's hair caught fire and he had to fight hard to free his hands in order to smother it.

It was at that moment that Major Dietrich arrived at the Joubert barn. Leon could hear the soldiers joking and laughing with their commander, clearly pleased with their results.

'Pigs!' one of the injured men screamed in response.

'Can you move, Guy?' Leon whispered to his neighbour.

Guy coughed as the smoke began to fill his lungs. His eyes were streaming but he nodded.

'Quick, try to get up, while they're distracted,' said Leon. 'I'm not going to let them burn me alive.'

As quietly as they could, and masked by the noise and smoke of the rapidly spreading fire, the two men wriggled free and crawled to a side door. Previously guarded by one of the soldiers, the door was now unattended.

Leon and Guy staggered out into the yard beyond, and were amazed to find that they were not alone. Four other men stood there, all but one of them with injured legs or arms, wildly looking around for a way out.

'Quick, over here,' hissed one of them, who was bleeding from his left arm. He had found a small hole in the crumbling far wall and was rapidly pulling at the loose stones to make the opening big enough to crawl through.

The others helped, and soon all six men squeezed themselves through into the garden on the other side.

'I can't run,' whimpered the last man through, collapsing onto the grass on the other side of the wall. Of the six, he was the most badly injured and was bleeding profusely from both legs.

'Get in here!' said Guy, pointing to some rabbit hutches lined up along the wall. 'They'll never look for you in there. Wait it out. We'll come back for you when it's all over. I promise you, my friend.'

The injured man climbed into the hutch and Leon covered it loosely with a tarpaulin which had been thrown over an old tractor, parked next to the barn.

Then the remaining five crept cautiously along the back wall of the barn.

Guy was limping badly. 'I think we should make a dash for it, across to the Peyrilhac road,' he whispered to the others. 'The smoke from the fire will give us some cover. It's blowing that way. Then we can head over the field behind the mill to the river. We can crawl if we have to. The grass is long enough to hide us.'

The others nodded. One by one, the first three darted across, and ran down a narrow alley between the houses, keeping lookout for one another to make sure they were not spotted.

Only Guy and Leon were left.

'I'm not coming with you,' said Leon flatly.

Guy looked at him, wide eyed.

'My family and I always said we would meet at the woods, behind the cemetery, if the Germans ever came. I might be the only one left alive, but I have to try to get there.'

'It's too far,' whispered Guy. 'You'll never make it.'

'I have to try,' Leon repeated, taking his neighbour's hand in his. 'And you must go. Good luck to you, Guy.'

The two men nodded at one another and shook hands, exchanging a brief, nervous smile, then went their separate ways.

22: THE HUNTER

LEON WATCHED as Guy made it safely across the street and disappeared down the alleyway. The ground where he had been standing just a few moments before was stained with blood and Leon swallowed hard, full of admiration at the bravery of his friend. He had lived next door to him for four years and had always thought him a friendly enough chap, but quite unremarkable. He was just an ordinary man, yet here he was, in the midst of a nightmare, acting so courageously. 'Please God,' Leon prayed silently, 'don't let him collapse before he makes it to the river. Give him a chance.' Then, as the image of Alfred sitting by that tree in the woods came back into his mind, he added, 'And please, I beg you, give *me* a chance. Help me find my son.'

The heat from the fire inside the barn was now so intense that Leon could feel it radiating through the stones of the wall behind him and thin fingers of smoke were beginning to creep through the cracks in the mortar. The air was rank with the burning smell and, as the breeze changed direction, the road temporarily cleared and the smoke began wafting instead across the garden into which Leon and his companions had first made their escape from the barn.

This was Leon's chance. It was now or never. Holding his breath he ran straight into the swirling grey fog, darting quickly across the end of Rue de la Cimetière and down an alleyway into the open space which lay in between the rear gardens of the buildings which lined the fairground. From there, he could sneak along the backs of the gardens and come out through one of the side alleyways further up on Rue de la Cimetière, hopefully away from danger.

As he emerged from the worst of the smoke, he looked across the open space in front of him and recognised the back wall of the Mayor's house. He sprinted over and, keeping low, ran along the wall and down the side passageway of the house. This led straight on to the fairground and Leon flattened himself against the wall to peer cautiously around the corner. He could see the well, where Sylvie and the children had waited for him earlier when they had tried to make their escape. The same German trucks were still parked there and Leon could see that they were unmanned. To his left he could make out soldiers going in and out of the houses on the other side of the field, still searching for survivors, some carrying petrol tanks ready to begin torching the buildings. But there was no one to his right.

Leon decided to cross the road again and head for the cornfield on the other side. There was a gap in the buildings there and only a small low fence which he would have to vault over. He knew he could do it and he had to be safer in the field than running up the road where he would have no cover at all.

He took one last glance to the left to check that no one was looking his way, and he ran.

From his hiding place in the cornfield, Alfred could hear the shooting at the Joubert barn and the screams and desperate cries under the gunfire. He covered his ears and screwed up his eyes tight to try to shut it all out. But try as he might, the noise still seemed to creep through his fingers, seeping into his brain, and he began to realise, from the pattern of sounds, that the same horrible things were happening all over his village.

He thought about his family. He wondered where the soldiers had taken Christelle and Sabine. And he thought about his friends, Ethan and Rachael, Patric, Jean, Pierre, Monsieur Lefevre and old Monsieur Demarais. Were they safe? Had they been shot? Were they lying somewhere, frightened, like he was?

Every so often, he dared to raise his head to peep out over the top of the corn. The cornfield sloped gently down towards Rue de la Cimetière, so while the corn was long enough to hide him while he lay flat, if he was careful he could lift himself up a little and get a clear view of the road and the entrance into the fairground through the gap in the buildings. Once or twice he had caught sight of some soldiers. They seemed to be working in pairs, and Alfred wondered if they were taking over all the houses and throwing people out, like they did in Charly, or whether they were looking for something. But why the shooting? What was that big explosion and what were they burning? It was all too much for him to understand.

The vile fumes from the Joubert barn were starting to stick in Major Dietrich's throat and make his eyes water. He took a handkerchief out of his pocket and wiped the dirt and sweat from his face then threw it onto the floor. He didn't want to arrive in Scholz's office in Limoges covered in soot and grease and with his uniform stinking of smoke. He was ready to move on. His work here was done.

The church was ablaze and he was satisfied that the male prisoners at all six locations had been dealt with. He would head back to his command post in the fairground and make sure his platoon leaders understood what they had to do before pulling out. His orders would remain unchanged: round up any stragglers, find and kill anyone who had managed to escape their search so far, and torch the rest of the village. This could be done without him. He had a more important job to do now: to report back to Major General Scholz, debrief him on the success of the mission, and spread the word. He would send out the message to the Resistance, to the whole of France, to the world, that no one could take on the SS without paying for it.

He imagined the praise he would get, the recognition, the admiration. This was his greatest achievement yet.

Dietrich strode up Rue de la Cimetière, a self-satisfied man, enjoying a sense of complete control. He had never felt so powerful, so indomitable.

So when the soot-blackened, bedraggled shadow of a man stumbled out from the alleyway and lurched across the road in front of him, he didn't call out 'Halt,' or try to apprehend him. He didn't want to question him. He could see he was a local and he didn't care who he was or what he was doing there in the street. He just shot him. One bullet. The side of the head.

The scream came from somewhere to his right. Somewhere up in the cornfield. A long-drawn-out, desperate, wailing, 'No!'

Dietrich scanned the field, seeing nothing at first. Then he spotted him. A small boy, maybe seven or eight, with red hair which flamed in the early evening sun. The boy was standing now, his mouth open, staring down first at him, as he stood with his revolver drawn, and then at the fallen man at his feet in the road.

Time seemed to be momentarily suspended while the two enemies, man and boy, stood there looking straight at one another. Then, like a hunted deer spooked by the sound of a breaking twig under the foot of his tracker, the boy turned and started to flee.

Dietrich followed, leaping easily over the fence and lunging hard into the knee-deep corn. The boy was moving as quickly as he could, desperate to stay out of reach, but he was running uphill and his short legs struggled to carry him any faster as they waded frantically through the foliage. He was no match for Dietrich, the experienced hunter, who was gaining fast.

A few more metres and the boy came to the edge of the crop. There was a strip of bare earth, about ten metres wide, then a small lane, and on the other side a wild meadow where the grass grew long and lush. Best to strike now. The boy was completely exposed and definitely in range. Dietrich halted, raised his revolver, aimed and fired.

The boy seemed to spin slightly in the air, then dropped to the ground.

Dietrich could hear no sound. No whimpering, no movement.

Slowly now, breathing deeply to regain his composure after the chase, Dietrich edged forwards to the spot where his prey had fallen.

The boy was lying twisted, half on his side, on the hard, red earth, one arm and his floppy red fringe partially covering his small pale face. Dietrich noticed that he had no shoes on his feet, and his shorts and shirt were filthy, as if he had been lying there out in the fields for a very long time.

Seconds passed, and Dietrich remained there, staring down at the young body he had just shot. How had this one little boy managed to escape the eyes of more than two hundred SS troops?

Keeping his revolver aimed, Dietrich nudged the boy hard in the back with his boot to see if he was still alive. He watched closely.

Nothing.

Dietrich smiled. Then he lowered his revolver, carefully replaced it in its holster and walked back down the hill. It was time to go.

PART 6

SATURDAY 10 JUNE, 1944 (EVENING)

23: THE FINAL TWO HOURS

IT WAS five o'clock when Major Dietrich sped out of Oradour. No longer concerned about being ambushed by the Resistance, he was driving himself in an open-topped jeep. He was heading for Limoges.

He had given his SS troops two more hours to clean up the village. He wanted every building checked one last time and his orders had been to shoot anyone found hiding, before burning the place to the ground.

Even without Dietrich's dominating presence and his ever-watchful gaze, the majority of the soldiers left behind were so fuelled by their commander's hatred of the Resistance and his cries for revenge for the murder of Major Klausner that they were more than happy to continue their violent rampage through the streets.

The silent minority of soldiers who couldn't convince themselves that the people in Oradour were guilty of anything nevertheless played their part in the evil. Driven by their fear of disobeying their ambitious, ruthless commander, they buried any doubts that they had about the murder of so many innocent men, women and children.

Rampaging through the houses and homes, businesses, offices and schools, the troops tore down doors, broke into cellars, ripped open crates and left little intact and nowhere to hide. Treasured possessions and family heirlooms were smashed or thrown to one side, while jewellery and smaller valuables found their way into soldiers' pockets. Beloved cats and dogs fled for cover or shot out of open doors in terror where they were left wandering the streets, searching in vain for their owners.

Two brothers sharing a car, on their way home from work in Confolens, were passing by Oradour on the road to the south of the river. Seeing so much smoke coming from the village, they abandoned their car and crossed the river by way of a footbridge, anxious to find out what was going on and to see if they could help. They didn't know that they were about to walk into a living nightmare. They were gunned down in the fairground, and their bodies thrown down the well.

And so, as the afternoon turned into evening, the slaughter continued.

Then, just before seven o'clock, the last tram of the day approached Oradour, bringing twenty-two villagers home from Limoges. The stunned passengers could hardly recognise the burning village that lay ahead of them and many of them got to their feet in panic.

The SS soldiers, who were getting ready to remove their road block near the bridge across the River Glane, their duty almost done, stopped the tram and ordered everyone to disembark.

The driver was instantly dragged to one side, a gun held to his head, a look of sheer dread in his eyes. The rest of the soldiers then encircled the passengers, their guns cocked and ready. Everyone was convinced that they were about to die.

Then one of the soldiers spoke, his French surprisingly good but with a heavy German accent.

'Oradour is no more,' he announced. 'Everyone is dead. But we are letting you live, so that you can tell the world what you have seen here tonight. The whole of France must learn. You cannot defeat the SS. You cannot resist us.'

He paused, to ensure that everyone understood. The small crowd remained silent. No one knew what to say or do.

'Now go. You are free.'

Some of the passengers wept, others clung onto one another, their knees weak with relief and sadness.

Prodding them in the back with their rifles, the soldiers ushered them back onto the tram. The driver was ordered to take them back to Limoges. He was not to stop until he got there.

As the tram pulled away, the passengers looked back over their shoulders at the devastation they were leaving behind them, a picture they would never forget, and they reached for one another's hands.

24: THE RIVER CROSSING

WHEN ALFRED poked his head up from the corn and recognised the familiar shape of his father emerging from the passageway onto the fairground, he forgot all about staying hidden. Without thinking, he jumped straight to his feet, ready to shout, 'Over here!' But before he could utter the words he saw the second shape, a tall sinister figure, wearing an SS officer's hat.

The German raised his gun and fired so quickly, so automatically, that by the time an anguished cry did come out of Alfred's mouth, his father was already on the ground, dead.

For a moment Alfred was too shocked to move, his feet as rooted to the soil as the corn stems all around him. He felt numb. He couldn't believe that what he had just seen was real. This couldn't be.

Then he realised that the German soldier was staring straight at him and he knew that it *was* real, and that he had to move, fast.

He could sense that his pursuer was gaining on him, but he couldn't run any quicker through the corn, and the leaves were slicing painfully at his legs. All he could do was keep on moving, and hope.

Alfred reached the top of the slope and was relieved to see that he was at the edge of the cornfield. If he could make it across this bare strip of land he could cross the lane and would then be in the meadow. He might be able to run more quickly downhill through the grass and from there it wasn't far to the trees along the river. They would give him some cover and he might be able to find somewhere to hide.

But then he heard the gunshot, and felt the bullet whistle through his shirt, grazing his waist. He glanced down at his side, and as he did so his toes caught on the uneven, baked earth and he tripped, twisting and grunting as he smacked down hard on the ground.

He could hear the German's heavy boots thundering up behind him and knew that if he moved, he would be killed. His only hope was to fool the German into thinking that he already had been. Mustering all his strength and courage, Alfred took a deep breath, covered as much of his face as he could with his arm, and played dead.

As the German stood over him, Alfred conjured up a happy, peaceful scene in his mind, of his family, all sitting around the kitchen table together eating some of his father's best pastries. He drew strength from the warmth of it and he felt his body relax. Whatever happened, there was no German in the world who could take away those memories from him. They were his, and he could always keep them safe.

So when he felt the hard sole of the officer's boot in his back, felt it rocking him, Alfred did not move. Not a single muscle.

It felt like the German would stand there looking at him for ever, and Alfred wondered what he was thinking. Why didn't he just shoot him, to be sure? But no shot came.

He had done it!

He listened to the footsteps moving away, off across the cornfield, back to the mayhem that was Oradour.

Too scared to move, Alfred lay there on the hard, unyielding earth for another two long hours. He was so terrified that the German would come back, or that he could be seen there on the hill by some of the other soldiers, he didn't even risk altering his position. He just stayed still, his eyes closed, trying not to cry and keeping himself calm by reliving in his mind all the adventures he had had around his village and picturing the faces of all the friends he had made while he had lived there. He stored each memory well, for he knew his life would never be the same again.

There was Patric, perched on an oil drum in the garage, sharing a story with him. Monsieur Demarais, dipping his nose into a large glass of his favourite red wine, and Monsieur Babin, shrieking with delight on the banks of the Glane as he reeled in his biggest ever catch. Alfred wondered if they were all gone. How many had been shot down in cold blood, like his father? How many were trapped inside those burning buildings? As long as he lived, Alfred would never forget them.

Suddenly, Alfred's thoughts were interrupted by a rushing sound in the cornfield behind him. Something was moving and it was coming towards him, fast.

Panic rushed through his veins. What if it was the same German officer, coming back to check whether he was really dead? His mind started working overtime, trying to remember whether, at any point during the last two hours, he had moved even the tiniest bit. Were his fingers, feet, in exactly the same position? Would the German remember?

The rustling was getting louder, closer. Then it stopped. Whoever it was was now right upon him, nudging his feet. Then Alfred nearly jumped out of his skin as a warm, hairy, wriggly little body leapt on top of him and started licking wildly at his ear. Bobby!

Alfred's first reaction was pure joy. Bobby was alive! This clever, plucky little dog had managed to stay safe through everything and, despite everything, had still managed to track him down. No wonder they called dogs 'faithful friends'. But this faithful companion was about to put him in grave danger.

'Ssh, Bobby. Lie still. You'll draw attention to us,' Alfred whispered, trying to calm Bobby down by stroking him smoothly down his back.

But it was clear that Bobby was way too happy to have found Alfred to lie down quietly. His tail had never wagged faster and his body was all of a tremble with the excitement.

Any time now he's going to bark, and then we're both done for, thought Alfred.

He knew that he couldn't stay where he was a moment longer. He and Bobby were totally exposed.

'Come on, Bobby,' he said quietly, getting to his knees. Bobby sat down, looking expectantly up into Alfred's face, his tongue lolling out of his mouth, his eyes hopeful.

'We're going for a run, got it? The most important run we've ever been on. And we've got to be quick. Do you understand, boy?'

Bobby wagged his tail as if he understood.

'Come on!'

Alfred and Bobby crossed the lane and set off down the hill through the meadow, heading straight for the tree line which followed the river bank. Alfred's legs were still slightly numb from lying in the same position on the ground for so long, and he stumbled a couple of times at first. Each time he did, Bobby jumped up playfully at his waist. Alfred knew that they were making far too much of a commotion but dared not look round. He just kept his eyes on the tree line and kept his legs and arms pumping.

By the time they were half way across the meadow, Bobby had run on ahead. Alfred saw him leap up to snap at a butterfly which fluttered above his nose. *Bless him, he's no idea of the danger we're in*, thought Alfred.

As he often did when they were out walking together, Bobby paused, turning to check that Alfred was still coming and to let him catch up. That was when he started barking. Not at Alfred. He was barking at something to Alfred's right, towards the houses on the road beyond Alfred's school. Soldiers.

'No, Bobby!' Alfred hissed, rushing towards the little black and white dog. 'Be quiet!'

In one movement, Alfred bent down and scooped Bobby up with his left arm as he continued to sprint through the grass.

Bullets whistled over their heads and Alfred ducked, sheltering Bobby as much as he could with his body and his right arm. Bobby gave out a little whimper.

'It's alright, boy,' Alfred said breathlessly into his soft pink ear. 'Nearly there.'

There was another stream of bullets but Alfred realised that this time the shots were way off their mark. The soldiers were too far away to get a good aim.

His bare feet were hurting badly now. Unprotected, they were bruised from the stones and hard, rugged ground, and covered in cuts and stings from the grasses and nettles they had run through. Tears were streaming down his face.

'Please, God,' he sobbed. 'Please let us make it.'

Ten more metres and, to Alfred's relief, they reached the tree line. He shot behind the trunk of a large oak, paused for a few seconds to catch his breath, then dared to peep back round. The meadow behind him was still clear, but he could see the two soldiers who had fired at them scrambling up onto a wall at the side of the road to get a better view. They seemed to be relaxed, as if they were sharing a joke, but clearly, Alfred and Bobby hadn't been forgotten. One of the two soldiers started scanning the tree line with a small pair of binoculars. Quickly, Alfred drew back behind the tree and looked down into Bobby's face.

'We can't stop yet,' he said, blinking away tears of frustration. 'We've got to cross the river. Come on.'

He gave the little dog a squeeze and kissed him on the head before placing him gently down on the ground. As he did so, a tear dropped onto the whiskery nose, and Bobby shook his head, comically.

'Now!' cried Alfred.

As soon as they started to move, the soldiers opened fire once again, glimpsing their movement among the shadows. Bullets strafed the tree trunks, and Alfred frantically looked up and down the river bank for a safe place to get down to the water.

'Here!' he shouted, half falling and half sliding down through the undergrowth, his arms and legs snagging on the brambles as he crashed to the bottom and into the cool water of the Glane.

He waded across the river, knee high at first where it rushed over shale, but reaching waist height where it meandered more sedately around the bend on the far side. Alfred could feel the cold numbing his toes and he nearly lost his footing more than once on the slippery stones, but he knew there was no going back.

He reached the other side, grappling among tree roots to pull himself up and out of the water. Dripping wet and exhausted, he flopped down on the bank and turned, ready to help Bobby.

The dog was still sitting on the other bank. Alfred's heart sank. How could he have forgotten? Bobby hated water. He never went in the river. Not even when he was with Patric.

'Oh come on, Bobby,' Alfred pleaded, gesturing to his little friend to follow him. 'You have to do it! Just this once. For me.'

But Bobby just sat there stubbornly, wagging his tail.

For a moment, Alfred contemplated getting back into the water. He would carry Bobby across if he had to. But then he saw the movement in the corner of his eye. The two soldiers. They must have come into the meadow to finish the job and they were now searching along the tree line.

Alfred looked back at Bobby. He had heard them too.

'Go!' whispered Alfred, pointing down the river, away from the approaching soldiers. 'Go, Bobby!'

Bobby looked from Alfred, to the soldiers, and back again. Then, to Alfred's relief, the little dog took off, running straight and fast, along the river bank and away from danger.

As quietly as he could, Alfred crept slowly up the slope, edging back inch by inch, until he disappeared into the shadows of the overhanging trees and was out of the soldiers' sight for good.

25: THE DEBRIEFING

ON THAT fine summer's day back in 1922, when his father had scolded him so harshly for jumping from the bridge into the river, Gustav had not screamed and shouted, even though he had wanted to. He had not let his father see him crying either, even though he desperately wanted him to know how much his words hurt, how much they wounded him. True, he had argued his case, but his pride had not allowed him to beg forgiveness. That he would never do. Instead, he would once again channel all his disappointment, all his anger, into finding another way to win his father's love, his affection, his pride.

The very same emotions now surged through Gustav Dietrich as he stood in front of Major General Scholz on that warm summer evening of 10th June 1944. He had arrived at Scholz's headquarters victorious, his entire body tingling with the expectation of the commendations he was about to receive. He had breezed into the hallway, and had even humoured that hair-brained receptionist, smiling at her while she telephoned through the news of his arrival to her boss and giggled at him when she showed him into the office. Yes, he was in a decidedly good mood.

Scholz had greeted him enthusiastically, showing Dietrich to his seat and encouraging him to get straight down to details. He trusted, he had said, that Dietrich's jubilant demeanour meant that the Oradour mission had been a success. But there were things he was anxious to know. Had Klausner's body been found? Were there any hidden weapons in the village? Had Dietrich needed to take the hostages?

Dietrich had held up his hand to stem the flow of questions, delighting in the drama of the moment. Then he had watched Scholz's expression gradually turn from elation to horror as he had described the events of the past few hours and, as he watched his superior's reactions, he had felt his own delight ebbing away.

'You knew Major Klausner was dead when you arrived in Oradour. And you knew that it was not Oradour where his body was found. Is that right, Dietrich?' asked Scholz, determined to get the facts clear.

'Yes, Major General. Thanks to my informants.'

'And yet you continued with the mission to search for him at Oradour?'

'Yes, Major General. I thought it likely that we would still find evidence linking Klausner's capture to Oradour. There could still have been weapons there.'

'And did you find anything?'

'No, Major General. But Oradour was so close to where it all happened. The villagers couldn't have been completely innocent.'

'Yes, they could!'

'Major General, Major Klausner was burned alive!' Dietrich stressed, unable to understand Scholz's clear disapproval. 'I knew that you would want to send out a message to the Resistance in response to that. We had the chance to make Oradour an example, to teach the rebels a lesson.'

'You had the chance, yes. But you did not have the authority!'

'My orders were to carry out a thorough search and we did that. Thoroughly. We left nothing behind. There was nowhere else to hide anything or anyone.'

'You burned that village to the ground, and everyone in it!'

Dietrich was becoming impatient. 'Major General, you gave me control of 3rd Company. I was the one there, in the field. I had to take the lead.'

'But, I repeat, your orders were only to search Oradour and, if you found nothing, to take hostages.'

'True. And I followed my orders. I negotiated with the Mayor of Oradour, but he refused to provide hostages. Negotiations failed.'

'I didn't order you to negotiate, Dietrich!' shouted Scholz, getting to his feet, his face red with anger. 'And I didn't give you permission to massacre hundreds of civilians! But I guess you will try to justify that, too!'

'I don't need to!' snapped Dietrich, saliva firing from his lips as he spoke, his fists clenched on the arms of the chair. 'History will prove I was justified when the Resistance falls apart. When the SS continues to move through France unhindered. When the whole of France accepts German occupation!'

For a moment the two men glared at one another, saying nothing, neither able to fully understand the other. Then Scholz slowly shook his head. He picked up his pen and, calmly now, took a piece of headed notepaper from his drawer. As he began writing, he spoke very clearly, without looking up from his page.

'Dietrich, this may end up costing you dearly. I'm going to ask the Division Court to instigate a court martial investigation against you at once. I cannot allow Das Reich to be charged with something like this.'

Furious, Dietrich opened his mouth to speak, then thought better of it, keeping the lid on the rage boiling inside him. There was no point in arguing with a man like Scholz. He had no idea what it meant to make real decisions, on the ground, when it really mattered. Surely the court martial investigation would see the logic in his decisions, and understand that his actions would bring victory to Germany, not shame.

'You are to file a detailed report,' Scholz continued, still not raising his gaze from the written order he was compiling. He didn't want to look Dietrich directly in the eye. He feared the evil he might see there, that it might infect him in some way. 'I want it on my desk within forty-eight hours. Now get out of my office.'

Only when Dietrich had slammed the door behind him did Scholz look up. He had had no hand in the horrors which this man had brought upon the innocent village of Oradour, no prior knowledge, but he knew that he could have prevented it. He hadn't liked Dietrich from the moment he had marched into his office. He had sensed his hot-headedness, his arrogance, his impulsiveness. The warning signs had been screaming at him. But Scholz had been losing his grip on the hostage situation and so he had ignored his doubts, clinging on to the hope that Dietrich was so hungry for recognition, so eager to please, that he would, in the end, succeed.

How did both of them get it so, so wrong?

PART 7

THURSDAY 29 JUNE, 1944
(DUSK)

26: THE FIGURE IN THE FOG

THE FURY that Dietrich felt when he left Major
General Scholz's office in Limoges soon turned to
despair. He had been convinced that Oradour would be
his moment of triumph, the pinnacle of his SS career.
How could it be that he was now facing interrogation
from the military court and being treated like a war
criminal? Why should he have to justify himself and
his actions? He was a decorated commander. Why
couldn't they trust his judgement? Why couldn't they
understand what he had done for them?

Before he joined the SS, Dietrich had never been completely content. It had seemed that nothing ever worked out as he planned or dreamed. He had lost his mother, the only person who had ever shown him any true affection; he had struggled so badly at school; and his relationship with his father had lurched from one disappointment to the next. No, life had not dealt him an easy hand – until he put on that SS uniform and became a soldier. Then he had found a place where he belonged, where his achievements were recognised and rewarded. In the army he felt needed and encouraged and, most important of all, he was never belittled.

But now his beloved institution was failing him. It was trying to shut him out, trying to distance itself from the events at Oradour. Dietrich couldn't imagine how he would endure the shame of the court martial. Win or lose, how could he ever hold his head up high again?

What would his father think?

Within forty-eight hours, Dietrich had filed his report with Scholz and then left with his battalion for Normandy. Nothing could be done until he had a court date, so he kept control of his troops, for now at least.

Sullen and withdrawn, he marched his men hard, eager to put as many miles between himself and Limoges as he could, as quickly as possible. But the distance did not help to lessen the weight of the dark cloud hanging over him and Dietrich arrived in Normandy depressed and morose.

His men saw the change in their commander and understood its cause well enough. Their leader's reputation was on the brink of destruction and, knowing that a wounded lion was a dangerous beast, they left him well alone. They followed his orders by day and kept their gossip quiet at night. They had a job to do, after all, and they had been with Dietrich long enough to know that he was usually on the winning side.

No one predicted that Dietrich would crumble. No one perceived that he had any weaknesses at all or believed that he would ever do anything but fight his corner. His men, his comrades, his superiors, even Scholz, assumed he would go into the court martial all guns blazing. That was his style.

So no one foresaw what happened late in the day on 29th June 1944 when, at the end of a long day's fighting in which his battalion had been holding off the British southern flank near Caen, Dietrich wandered out beyond enemy lines. Leaving a command post shelter like that, without wearing a helmet and during such heavy bombardment, was pure suicide, everyone said afterwards. What was the Major thinking? He would never normally be so reckless.

Major Gustav Dietrich was hit in the head by artillery shell splinters as he walked out, all alone, into the crossfire, his revolver dangling limply at his side, completely unprepared for combat. He fell, face down in the grass, blood streaming down his face.

As he lay there flickering in and out of consciousness, Dietrich's confused mind took him back and forth from the present to the past, the pictures it created so real he felt he could touch them. He recalled when he had had lain injured on another patch of French soil, his lungs pierced by bullets, dangerously close to death. Then he was pulled back to the present and he found himself calling, once again, to that eerie figure in the fog, the faceless grey figure who in neither his finest nor his darkest hours would ever come close to him.

Dietrich's eyes closed now, and he was surprised to discover that he was upright again, standing looking down on his own wounded body. He was curious to know if he was alive or dead, so he flipped the body over, shoving it with his foot. But as the body rolled to stare up at the sky, it wasn't his own face that he saw, it was the angelic face of a boy. That small, gutsy red-headed boy whom he had shot in that cornfield in Oradour.

The one who pretended to be dead.

Dietrich thought how close he had come to ending

the boy's daring game, to firing into his skull and snuffing out his life as he had that of so many others. What would it have mattered? He hadn't known him and he didn't care who he was. But as he had gazed down at his still little form, Dietrich had seen himself as a boy of the same age, wanting to make his father proud with his courage and ingenuity. He had seen in this young French boy his own hopes and dreams, and he had both pitied and admired him. So he had lowered his gun and, for the first time, spared the life of another. *If this boy dies today*, he had thought, *it will not be by my hand*. And he had turned and walked back towards the burning skyline of Oradour.

The grey figure was getting closer now, his woollen suit becoming clearer through the fog. Dietrich started to feel cold, his legs and fingers numb, and a shudder ran through his body, causing his eyes to flicker open once more. The fog was lifting and silence seemed to have fallen on the battlefield. Dietrich could see the figure's face so clearly now he could almost touch it.

So familiar.

Maybe now.

Maybe this time.

Dietrich reached out his arm, his long, slender fingers stretching, pleading for the figure to take his hand, but the light was fading so quickly. He tried to move his lips and he heard his own voice, faint and rasping, whispering, 'Wait! I need to know. I have to…'

He wanted to keep his eyes open to see, but it felt like someone or something was pressing them closed. All that was left was darkness, silent darkness. Gustav Dietrich's time had run out.

PART 8

EPILOGUE

28: THE TRUE STORY OF ORADOUR-SUR-GLANE: AUTHOR'S NOTES

Ten years ago, I spent a day in the memorial village of Oradour-sur-Glane in the Haute-Vienne region of France. It was a day which almost happened by chance but it became a day I would never forget.

I was in France visiting my sister-in-law. She had recently moved into the area and was telling me about places of interest near to her new home in Confolens. She happened to mention a village not far away which had been destroyed by the Nazis during the Second World War. The whole place was left in ruins, she told me, unchanged since the moment the Germans walked away.

Now, I love history, and thought myself fairly well acquainted with the key events of the Second World War, but here was a story which was completely new to me. I had to go and find out more.

Although I spent only a few hours walking the haunting ruins at Oradour-sur-Glane, the impact of my visit left images ingrained on my soul, snapshots of an extraordinary event that were to stay with me for years to come, and which would keep drawing me back. I wanted to know more about the ill-fated cast of the tragedy that took place in the village on that day in June 1944 – the locals, the day visitors, the men, women and children, and the SS soldiers who took their lives. And most of all, I wanted to know the story of one particular character, whose face in an old black and white photograph captivated me and whose image was, to me, more powerful than any other. Roger Godfrin. The only child among the mere twenty-nine survivors, he did not follow German orders to assemble in the centre of the village and had the courage and the wisdom to make an escape, climbing out of a window of his school.

Roger was just seven and three-quarters when the massacre took place. In the photograph, taken soon after, he is back in Oradour-sur-Glane, posed rather uncomfortably among the rubble. Trench coat fastened, shirt buttoned right up to the collar, thick knee-high socks pulled up smartly, his red fringe neatly combed down under his beret. His young face, his eyes, carry a frown yet his mouth is slightly twisted, as if he is uncertain whether to smile for the camera. What a brave little soul he must have been. The boy who fooled the SS, who chose his own path to safety but was to discover, at the end of it, that he had been left an orphan. He was photographed when the trauma must have still been so raw, back in the place where his mother, his father, his three sisters and his younger brother had been murdered, just months before.

As I studied this photograph again and again, the questions started to form. How had a boy of seven found the courage and discipline to lie motionless in a field for two hours while German soldiers ransacked his village? What must have been going through his mind? Why did he refuse to go to the assembly point like everyone else and decide, instead, to escape? And what kind of man could take aim and shoot at a little boy who was running away?

Weaving the truth about what happened to the people in Oradour-sur-Glane on 10th June 1944 into a fictional

231

story presented one crucial challenge. It would be all too easy to shy away from revealing the true extent of the SS soldiers' cruelty. It might be less risky, too, to change some of the more gruesome details out of fear of upsetting the reader. But to do either of those two things would be to do a disservice not only to those who lost their lives or lost loved ones that day, but also to the reader. For this is a story which can open the reader's eyes to the extremes of human behaviour. It can hold up a mirror to a world in which, side by side, there can exist a man like Gustav Dietrich, who is willing to order the mass slaughter of hundreds of innocent people, and a seven-year-old boy like Alfred Fournier, who has the courage and sheer determination to survive against all odds while his world is turned upside down around him. And it is a story inspired by true events from which we can still learn much, even though they happened nearly seventy years ago.

Just before two o'clock on the afternoon of Saturday 10th June 1944, twenty Waffen-SS officers and 187 Waffen-SS soldiers marched into the French village of Oradour-sur-Glane, sealing off all the roads in and out of the village as they did so.

It was the day before the religious festival of Corpus Christi, and the residents were in a festive mood. It was also the day on which the tobacco rations were brought into the village. That, combined with some medical vaccinations taking place in the school, meant that the village was busier than usual, with many children coming into Oradour-sur-Glane from outlying farms and villages as well as day visitors who had come to enjoy a leisurely lunch, a bit of shopping or some fishing on the River Glane.

Although they were surprised at the sight of German troops arriving, the majority of the people in Oradour-sur-Glane that day were not unduly concerned. The village had a reputation for being relatively peaceful and had enjoyed little interference from the German occupying army.

So when everyone in the village was summoned to assemble in the market square (known as the fairground) for an identity check, the majority saw no reason not to cooperate. Only about twenty people decided to make themselves scarce, and most of these were people who had more reason than most to be suspicious of the German army, such as the Jewish and French refugee families who had made their homes in Oradour.

One such family were the Godfrins, upon whom the fictional Fournier family is based. The Godfrins had come to Oradour four years earlier after being evicted from their home in Charly, in the Lorraine region of

France. Of the five Godfrin children, three (Jeanne, age thirteen, Pierette, eleven, and Roger, seven) were at school that afternoon. All had been warned by their mother and father to flee if the Germans ever came to Oradour, but only Roger (the inspiration for the story's young hero, Alfred) heeded that warning and escaped out of a back door of the school.

The soldiers of the 3rd Company of the 1st Battalion of Der Führer Regiment who came to Oradour-sur-Glane were under the command of Sturmbannführer Adolf Diekmann, a well-respected SS major with an excellent military record – his awards included the Iron Cross 2nd and 1st Class. In our story, Diekmann becomes Gustav Dietrich.

Many of the details in this book are based on survivors' accounts of events that afternoon. We know that Diekmann liaised with the Mayor of Oradour, Paul Desourteaux, while his troops moved through the village making sure that everyone went to the fairground.

It took less than an hour for the majority of residents and visitors to be assembled in the fairground, and soon after the men were separated from the women and children. It is understood that Diekmann explained to the assembled crowd that the SS suspected there was a secret store of arms somewhere in Oradour and demanded that anyone who had any information, or who possessed any such weapons, should come forward, but it is not known for certain whether this took place before or after the women and children were taken to the church.

It is also uncertain whether it was before or after this that Diekmann asked the Mayor to nominate hostages and accounts also vary as to the number of hostages he requested. Some historians put the figure at thirty while others as many as fifty, but all agree that Desourteaux refused to do so, offering himself and his four sons as hostages instead.

Once the women and children had been taken to the church, the men were taken to six different locations around the village. For the purposes of the story, the exact location of some of these sites has been moved and various fictional characters, including Leon Fournier, have been placed in specific locations in order to provide a pair of eyes through which events could be retold. However, the following details are generally known to be accurate.

The largest group of men (estimated at sixty-two) was taken to the Laudy Barn in the centre of the village. We know most about this location because it was from here that five men, including nineteen-year-old Robert Hébras, escaped.

The second location was the Milord Barn, located on the main road through the village, Rue Emile Desourteaux. We are not sure how many men lost their lives here, but of the six execution sites, this was located the closest to the church.

The third barn which was used belonged to the Bouchoule family and, as in the story, it was the site which was furthest away from the main village, near to the watermill on the River Glane. Among the bodies found here were the remains of a few women and children and some historians have suggested that these could be victims who escaped from the church or who were rounded up later.

The next execution site was the garage belonging to Hubert Desourteaux, son of the Mayor, which was located on the Rue Emile Desourteaux. No one is certain how many men died here and the murder of Patric Depaul here, in the story, is a piece of fiction. Hubert Desourteaux was, in fact, one of the few survivors from the Oradour massacre. He was an escaped prisoner of war so had good reason not to follow the SS soldiers' orders to go to the fairground, opting instead to hide in the garden of the Desourteaux house, where he stayed until night fell before escaping from the village.

The fifth location chosen by Diekmann and his men was a wine store belonging to a Monsieur Denis just off the Rue Emile Desourteaux on the road to Saint Junien. The remains of both men and women were found in a pit hastily dug by the SS soon after the massacre in the garden next to the store. But only one was identifiable, the body of the Mayor. He had been hit by two bullets in the chest, which had passed straight through his wallet.

The Beaulieu forge or blacksmith's workshop was the final site. About twenty-five bodies were found here.

Around four o'clock, a signal – described by some as an explosion, by others as a gunshot – could be heard all over Oradour. This was the sign that the massacre was to begin. In the church, where over four hundred women and children were crammed together, an incendiary device (a crate full of asphyxiating ammunition) was set off, filling the nave with smoke and fumes. It has been suggested that the Germans intended to suffocate the women and children with this device but that the attempt failed. Whether or not this was the case, any women or children who tried to escape the fumes were shot, and then shots were also fired at the crowd gathered in the nave. The soldiers also threw hand grenades into the terrified crowd. Firewood, straw and wooden chairs were piled on top of the bodies and set alight by the German soldiers, some of whom were as young as eighteen.

The fictional character of Audrey Rousseau is loosely based on a true heroine from Oradour. Only one person survived the massacre in the church that day, Madame Marguerite Rouffanche, who climbed out of a window. She was followed by a woman with a baby, Madame Joyeux, but they were both killed when the Germans saw them escaping and opened fire. Madame Rouffanche was shot five times, but she managed to make her way into a nearby garden where she was found at about five o'clock the next day, still covered in soot and crying out, 'I am suffering too much. Carry me to the river, I want to die!'

Carried in a wheelbarrow to a nearby doctor, Madame Rouffanche was to remain in hospital in Limoges for nearly a year, recovering from her physical injuries and from the mental trauma of an ordeal in which her daughter had been gunned down in front of her eyes.

While Oradour church saw the largest number of deaths on one site that tragic afternoon, the horror suffered by the men and boys at the six other sites around the village was no less shocking. Machine guns had been posted at the entrance to each site, and on the four o'clock signal, the SS soldiers opened fire, aiming not to kill but to strike low, so as to injure and maim. The bodies were then covered in hay and bundles of firewood, before being set alight.

Most of our information about what happened during this part of the massacre comes from one of the five survivors from Madame Laudy's barn. Robert Hébras (who inspired the character of Guy Dupont), escaped through a stable and into a yard where he found four other escapees. One of these men, a stonemason named Mathieu Borie, noticed that some of the stones in the wall were not cemented in very well and began to remove them, one by one, until he had made a hole large enough for the five men to climb through into another barn. Once there, they managed to stay hidden in a hay loft until two soldiers came in and set this alight also. Still undetected, the five men, three of whom – including Robert – were injured, escaped into a yard where they hid in a poultry hut. Later, at about seven o'clock, they crept out and got safely out of Oradour by way of the fairground and the road to the cemetery.

The amazing story of Alfred Fournier's escape follows very closely the accounts given by Roger Godfrin when he was interviewed as a witness at the 1953 trials of the SS soldiers involved in the massacre. Roger's family had an agreed plan that, if the Germans ever came to Oradour-sur-Glane, they would all go to hide in the woods behind Oradour cemetery. Their previous experience in fleeing from Charly in 1940 had taught them never to trust their German enemy.

On the afternoon of 10th June, Roger was at the Lorraine refugee school on the road to Peyrilhac with his two eldest sisters, Jeanne and Pierette. When the sound of machine guns was first heard, their teacher, Monsieur Goujon, originally took his pupils to the infants' school, further up the road into the village and closer to the church. It was into this classroom that the German soldier arrived to order the staff and children to join the rest of the villagers on the fairground.

Despite Roger's pleas, his sisters decided to obey the soldier's order, crying that they wanted to be with their mother. We do not know why Roger's parents, Arthur and Georgette did not stick to the plan that day, nor do we know exactly what happened to his youngest two siblings, Claude (age four) and Josette (age three). All we do know is that their names appear alongside those of his two elder sisters on the memorial plaque to the forty-four refugees from Charly in Lorraine who lost their lives that day.

Having made his decision not to follow his sisters to the fairground, Roger, who had a reputation for being a bit of a daredevil, took advantage of a moment when the SS soldier who had come to round them up was distracted. While the German was talking to Monsieur Goujon, Roger sneaked out of the classroom into a play room on the back of the school and then out of an open window. He climbed a fence behind the school, losing a shoe as he did so, but then, hearing two German sentries laughing and joking, was forced to hide. He was joined in his hiding place by Monsieur Thomas, his father's boss, and three others.

Roger stayed hidden there for some time, but when he heard the machine gun fire breaking out all over the village, he fled for the cemetery. As he reached the corner of the road to the cemetery, he was spotted by a soldier who fired at him. In our story, this soldier becomes Dietrich, fresh from the murder of Alfred's father, and this is the only moment in which the two central characters meet.

Roger's next move was, for a seven-year-old boy, incredibly brave and showed amazing presence of mind. Having been shot at, Roger fell to the ground and pretended to be dead, successfully fooling the soldier who even kicked him in the kidneys to see if he moved.

Roger lay there for more than two hours before continuing his race for the woods. Even so, he was spotted by another German soldier. Luckily this man showed him some mercy, telling him to run away fast, rather than shooting at him. It may have been at this point that Roger decided to change his route, abandoning his attempt to reach the woods behind the cemetery and to head instead for the River Glane.

His new route was safer, leading him through long grass, and it was here that he was joined by a black and white dog called Bobby who ran with him. But as the pair approached the river, six soldiers in a truck saw them from the road and opened fire. Roger dived across the river to safety and, suffering scratches to his body and thighs from the brambles on the river bank, hid behind a large oak tree, while the little dog was not so lucky.

Roger Godfrin was the only school child in Oradour-sur-Glane that day who survived the massacre by the SS. After the horrific event, he returned to the ruined village several times for special commemoration events and the photographs taken of him, standing among the ruins and the memorials in the cemetery, came to symbolise the many innocent victims who lost their lives that day.

After the war, in the early 1950s, Roger became an Air Force cadet and went on to marry and have two children of his own. Right up until his death at the age of sixty-four, on 10th February 2001, he always played down the bravery of his actions that day in 1944. It was, he said, 'Just fate, I did like the others did. Cleverer ones died in it. It's just destiny, nothing heroic at all.'

Of the 644 people who lost their lives in Oradour-sur-Glane, 191 were men, 247 were women and 206 were children. Almost 170 were people from the surrounding villages and hamlets who were either rounded up and brought to the fairground by the SS or who were in Oradour on 10th June voluntarily. Many of these were school children who had come into Oradour for the vaccination programme being carried out that day. Another thirty-three of the victims came from Limoges and twenty-five were from other parts of the Haute-Vienne. Only eighty-six residents of Oradour survived, fifty-seven of whom were not in the village that day and twenty-three of whom, including Roger Godfrin, escaped death by hiding around the village or by fleeing to safety. Only six people escaped from the execution sites: the five men who fled from the Laudy Barn, and Madame Rouffanche, who climbed out of the church window.

According to the museum at the Memorial and Visitor Centre at Oradour-sur-Glane, the blame for the massacre is laid firmly at the door of General Heinz Lammerding, Commander of the Das Reich division. Indeed it is his name that appears on a plaque in the cemetery which bears the inscription:

'Crime committed by the 2nd SS Division Das Reich under orders of General Lammerding.'

Furious about the increase in Resistance attacks and under pressure to move the troops rapidly north to Normandy to defend against the Allied invasion, Lammerding had, on 5th June 1944, issued an anti-terrorist memorandum in which he outlined the repressive measures to be taken against civilians in areas in which the Resistance was operating. In response to this and to a Resistance attack on a garrison at Tulle, near Limoges, Lammerding had ordered the hanging of ninety-nine male hostages from the village.

The abduction and kidnap of the SS commander Major Helmut Kämpfe (upon whom the character Major Thomas Klausner is based) led Lammerding to issue a further Order of the Day, dated 10th June, called 'The Position with Regard to Guerrilla Bands and Tactics for Combating Them'. This order outlined the punitive measures to be taken against anyone who threatened the established order of the German occupation. There was to be a 'brutal crackdown in the zone'.

However, whether or not that specifically ordered the massacre which took place in Oradour-sur-Glane is the subject of much debate.

According to the Police Superintendent Massièras in his testimony at the Bordeaux trials in 1953, the Germans were keen to take reprisals for the murders of Kämpfe and the driver of Karl Gerlach (Gerlach becomes Heinz Goth in our story) and 'wanted to terrify the French people.' He suggests that Oradour-sur-Glane was an ideal target for a reprisal as, 'they could not do so in a town of 10,000 inhabitants [like Saint Junien] but they could do so in a village'.

Other historians agree that Oradour-sur-Glane was specifically chosen as a target by the Nazis because of its size, and they also point to the fact that it was defenceless and easy to encircle. Certainly, the village was only a few kilometres from the place where Kämpfe was ambushed, and according to Karl Gerlach, his abduction and narrow escape from execution also took place in the vicinity of Oradour.

So there were clear reasons to search the area, and maybe even to demand hostages in order to negotiate with the Resistance, but there is no solid evidence linking Oradour-sur-Glane to any Resistance activity, and no documented proof that Lammerding specifically ordered the massacre of innocent civilians here. Even if Major Adolf Diekmann did have orders to search the village and take hostages, it is quite possible that he was not ordered to do any more than that. This is why many historians and commentators on the massacre at Oradour-sur-Glane point the finger of blame primarily at this man.

Sturmbannführer Adolf Diekmann was described by his superiors as a 'very brave, go-getter' who was 'very deliberate in the leadership of his Battalion'. He could be short-tempered and brusque with his men and there are even suggestions that he was a drinker (although this is not backed up by the official assessment of his character which was made and documented by his superior, Sylvester Stadler, just a few days before the massacre, on 1st June 1944).

Diekmann is reported to have been enraged about recent Resistance attacks, and his own battalion had been one of their targets while crossing the Dordogne on their march north. Diekmann and his fellow SS commanders were also furious about the abduction and kidnap on 9th June of the SS commander Major Helmut Kämpfe, a man whom he is reported to have known well, and to have fought alongside.

So when he was given orders from his regiment to go into Oradour and search for Kampfe and to take hostages, it is quite likely that Diekmann relished the opportunity to take revenge. According to massacre survivor Robert Hébras in his book *The Slaughter of our Village*, Diekmann took matters into his own hands in Oradour, going way beyond his orders in his lust for retribution:

'The decision had been taken to carry out a punitive operation, it appears, by the senior staff of the Das Reich division. Its organisation and execution were entrusted to Diekmann … I am also persuaded that

Diekmann went beyond the initial order, as could be proved by the sadism with which he exterminated the women and children.'

We cannot be sure whether Diekmann knew that Major Kämpfe had been murdered by the time he entered Oradour, but it does seem that the meeting he had in Saint Junien, just a couple of hours before the first troops arrived in the village, was crucial in some way. If Diekmann received news about Major Kämpfe from his informants at that meeting, it could have influenced his decision not to take hostages, as ordered, but to seek revenge instead.

Certainly, when Diekmann returned to the headquarters of the Der Führer Regiment in Limoges at the end of the day on 10th June, we hear that his commanding officer, Stadler, was 'shaken to the core' by his report. Not only did Stadler consider Diekmann's actions to be a huge overreaction to events, he was also quick to insist that Diekmann would have to face a court martial. 'I cannot allow the regiment to be charged with something like this!' Stadler is reported to have said.

However, Diekmann did not live long enough to face a court martial. He was killed just nineteen days after the massacre on the battlefield in Normandy, so we can never know the real reasons behind his appalling actions.

In the days, weeks and months after it happened, the massacre at Oradour-sur-Glane shocked the whole of France, and in 1953 in Bordeaux, it led to one of the most significant series of post-war trials of German officers.

Although many of the accused, including Diekmann, were dead or missing, eight German SS soldiers were present at the trial, alongside fourteen soldiers from the Alsace who had taken part in the massacre. Forty-four men were also tried *in absentia* (in their absence).

Diekmann's death on the Normandy battlefield in 1944 made him an easy scapegoat for the atrocities. Since he was not present to defend himself to the French courts, it was simple to blame him for everything as the commander of the exercise.

General Lammerding was also absent. By then he was living in Düsseldorf, in an area which fell under British authority. Before they would agree to allow the French courts to summon Lammerding to trial, the British authorities demanded strong proof of guilt. They were keen to ensure that the trial was genuinely about bringing justice and was not simply a way of seeking revenge. In Lammerding's case, the French courts could not convince the British authorities that there was sufficient evidence to prove his involvement in the massacre at Oradour-sur-Glane, and so their request to extradite him was declined. Lammerding did, however, send a letter to the courts in which he confirmed that he had been informed by Commander Sylvester Stadler that Adolf Diekmann had exceeded his orders at Oradour, and that he would have faced an enquiry, had he not been killed before it took place.

In the end, all the 46 accused, including Lammerding, who were not present at the trial were sentenced to death 'in absentia'. The rest were given prison sentences of between eight and twelve years, with the German defendants being given longer sentences than the Alsatians.

The verdicts created uproar. Many thought they were far too lenient while others, who argued that the SS were reacting to attacks by the Resistance and that they were carrying out Diekmann's orders, claimed that they were far too severe.

Amazingly, the latter won the day as, following a series of protests which led to an amnesty, all twenty-one men were soon released. This decision was met with outrage by the survivors of Oradour-sur-Glane who felt that their village was being punished and sacrificed for a second time.

The people of Oradour-sur-Glane may yet get some justice. At the end of 2011, the German police raided the homes of six men, all aged between 85 and 86 years old and all known to have belonged to the 3rd Company of the 1st Battalion of Der Führer in the SS Das Reich division, which carried out the atrocities at Oradour-sur-Glane on 10th June 1944. No names have been released but it has been suggested that these men did not stand trial at Bordeaux in 1953.

During the raids, the police searched for wartime documents, photographs, diaries and any other evidence which might prove the role that these men played in the massacre. All of the men arrested were low-ranking officers and two have denied taking part in the murders, while the other four have declared themselves unfit to be questioned.

However, investigations continue and if sufficient evidence is found, the accused could be put on trial for murder or accessory to murder.

For now, the men who killed so many innocent men, women and children at Oradour-sur-Glane may have escaped punishment, but their actions – and the lessons learned from them – will never be forgotten. The stories of the survivors, of people like Roger Godfrin, Marguerite Rouffanche and Robert Hébras, serve to teach us about the very worst and the very best of human nature.

The original village of Oradour-sur-Glane was never rebuilt. Left as they were, the ruins were seen as far more powerful – a symbol of France's suffering during the war. However, in 1946, two years after the country was liberated from German occupation, the National Assembly authorised the construction of a new town, adjacent to the old. Completed in 1953, when the first few families moved in, the new Oradour provided a fresh start, a new beginning, and yet no one who lived there could – or wanted to – forget the past. The new town would remain a place of mourning for many years to come and there were never any public festivals or celebrations held there, only memorial events for the old town.

It was not until the early 1960s that the residents felt able to begin building a new social life for the town, starting with the construction of a recreation hall which could be used for youth activities and events. Gradually, new blood began to move in and, as the years went by, the town became less restrained by its past. That great healer, time, had led the people of Oradour to a place where they could finally begin to look more positively to the future.

I leave you with the words of survivor Robert Hébras, who still lives close to Oradour-sur-Glane in Saint Junien. Although in his late eighties, Hébras continues to conduct tours of the ruins and, in 2011, helped to make a documentary feature film about the tragedy, called *Une Vie Avec Oradour* (*A Life With Oradour*). In an interview Hébras gave in April 2002, he spoke about finding that balance between remembering the past and being able to move on:

'It takes time. It takes time. Time has to pass, as one says... I understand very well that people from my generation may not like (if one can put it that way) to remember defeat. But on the contrary, I think they should tell their children and their grandchildren what happened. These generations want to know, understand. But we shouldn't point the finger of blame ... no army in the world has only good or all bad sides. We must forgive, but perhaps it is necessary to forget some things to get over it.'

AUTHOR'S ACKNOWLEDGEMENTS

I would like to thank the following people for their help and support with the production of this book.

For reading my manuscript, giving me their honest opinion and offering so many words of encouragement: My mum and dad – Irene and David Watts, John and Carolyn Gallagher, my nephew Adam Gallagher, Keith and Merle Yeomans, Kate Whyman, teachers Joy Redrup and Stephanie Cerrone, and Stratford-upon-Avon School's librarian.

Helen Fry, for first taking me to Oradour-sur-Glane and starting me on this journey, and for her hospitality, fantastic farm cooking and supply of French wine on our subsequent visits there. Thanks also to David, Tom and Anna Fry for entertaining the tribe that came with me on those weekends in France.

Michael Williams, for creating the informative website www.oradour.info and for his passion for detail.

Author Tony Bradman, for helping me to find a fabulous publisher and editor, and for the writing workshop which inspired me to 'have a go'.

The staff at the Centre de la Mémoire in Oradour-sur-Glane, for providing such a powerfully moving, respectful and informative on-site exhibition.

Robert Hébras, survivor of the massacre, for continuing to keep alive the memory of those lost, not least through the published account *The slaughter of our village* which he co-wrote with André Desourteaux and which was such a valuable source of detail.

Kate Paice at Bloomsbury, for her advice and ideas, for her incredibly sensitive and brilliant editing, and for giving me the opportunity to turn my vision into reality.

My children, Jack and Georgia, for putting up with so many 'quick' dinners and un-ironed clothes while I worked on this book.

And finally my husband, Jon, for being my sounding board and for his constant and unquestioning support, from the moment I decided to write this book right up to the moment when I typed the final full stop.